The Chantry Pr

Alfred J

Edition : Culturea (Hérault, 34)
Contact : infos@culturea.fr
Print in Germany by Books on Demand
Design and layout : Derek Murphy
Layout : Reedsy (https://reedsy.com/)
ISBN : 9791041951321
Légal deposit : September 2023

OF THE ABBEY OF ST. ALBAN, OF OFFA, OF MATTHEW OF PARIS

The third day of June, 1468.

I HAVE dwelt in this Abbey for the space of five years with fair report, as I trust, from them that bear rule therein, and not wholly barren, of good works done for the glory of God and for the honour of this pious foundation. And because this Abbey was for many generations renowned as a seat of learning and letters, in which, if I may be suffered to speak in a Pagan fashion, while all the Muses have been worshipped, special honour bath been had to the Muse of history, I purpose to write down certain things which they that shall come after me shall think it not lost labour to read. But I shall be content to write only the things which I have myself seen, or wherein I have taken a part. Of the history of this realm or of the other kingdoms of Christendom I do not presume to speak, not counting myself equal to them who in this place have dealt with such things, such as were Roger of Wendover, Matthew Paris, Thomas Rishanger, and Thomas Walsingham. But though these matters are too high for me, and, indeed, at least in these present days, are best treated by one that doth live, not in the cloister, but in the world, of lesser things I do not fear to write. For that which seemeth of small account in the present doth often become exceeding precious by mere passage of time. Even as we do count the silver cups which Abbot Warren, in the days of King Richard the First, gave to the house, though they be both small and thin, as of more value than the great bowl of silver gilt which was bought but last year, so we do love to read of little things, so they be of times long past, rather than of great things which are present with us.

First, then, I will write, but that very briefly, of this Abbey of St. Alban wherein He who ordereth the affairs of men hath cast my lot. 'Tis a house of the Benedictines, which Offa, King of Mercia, second of the name, did found about the year of our Lord seven hundred and ninety and three. This Offa was warned of God in a dream that he should search out the relics of St. Alban—that was Christ's first martyr in this realm—and lay them in a suitable place. Then the King, desiring to obey the heavenly vision, communicated the thing to Humbert, Archbishop of Lichfield, and, by his counsel, journeyed to the town of Verulam, the same that is now called St. Alban's, a great company of men, women, and children following him. Nor had he need to search long time for that which he sought, for he saw (as may be read in the Greater Chronicle of Matthew Paris) a ray of light, like unto a great torch, come forth from the sky, and fall, as might a flash of lightning, upon the burial-place of the martyr. (This Alban, I should say, was a Roman soldier in the camp that was in old time in the town of Verulamium, and made confession of his faith, even unto death, in the days of Diocletian the Emperor.) Now there had been a church of stone built in this same place by St. German, Bishop of Auxerre, in the year of our Lord four-hundred-and-thirty, of which Baeda, surnamed the Venerable, writes that it was of a marvellous beauty; which church had been wholly destroyed by the Saxons, so that not one stone of it was left. Hence it had come to pass that a place before known of all was now known of none. But now King Offa being, as I have shown, divinely led, found a coffin of wood, and in the coffin the bones of the Saint, and with these, relics of all the apostles and of other martyrs which St. German had caused to be placed therein. And all the people wept for joy when they saw this thing. Afterward the archbishop and bishops carried the bones very reverently to a certain church without the town, and laid them in a shrine made of gold and silver and precious stones. After this, King Offa journeyed to Rome, where, when he had visited all the holy places, he made his petition to Adrian I., being at that time Pope, for help and favour in the building of a house for monks in honour of St. Alban. This the Pope willingly promised, saying that he should take counsel with his bishops and nobles as to the possessions and privileges which he was minded to give to the said house, and that he, the Pope, would confirm all such gifts, and would adopt it for a daughter of the Roman Church, and subject it to his own jurisdiction, exempting it from all other.

So the King, having returned to his realm of England, called together a council of his bishops and nobles at Verulam, and, with their consent, founded this house, bestowing upon it many possessions, both of lands and benefices, and also many privileges, of which the chief was this—that it should have power to collect from the whole county of Hertford all the moneys commonly called Peter's pence, and to divert them to its own use.

So much having been said of the foundation of this house, it followeth to speak very shortly of its outward aspect. On the north side is the great church, with which for length none in this realm can compare, and for magnificence but few only. Of the first building of this church, of that which hath been added thereto or changed therein, there is no need to speak; for it is, as I suppose, known to every man. On the south side of the church are the cloisters, and to the east of these the chapter-house where the brethren meet daily for counsel and edification, and to choose to vacant places, when there chance to be such. And next to the chapter-house is the great dormitory, and under this the chamber of those that have been bled (for every monk must lose blood twice in the year, except the leech forbid for his health's sake). On the one side of the dormitory is a chapel, and on the other the refectory. Eastward, near to the Holywell Gate, is the infirmary, with a cloister of wood and a fair garden, wherein the sick may walk for their health. And to the south of the refectory is the kitchen, with other offices, among which is the sartory, or tailor's shop. (For it is a rule of St. Benedict, who established our order, that every house should suffice for itself, having within itself all necessary trades, so that there should be no occasion for the service of strangers.) Besides these there is a great square with cloisters all about it, and a conduit of water in the middle, and a place for washing. And there are many other buildings, of which there is no need to speak, save only to mention the Abbot's lodging and his guest-house, very fine and stately, as it must needs be, since it hath ever been the custom of the house to entertain many great and noble guests.

But I must not forget to note the great court of the Abbey, which lieth to the westward and the southward of the church. This is girt about with a wall very high and strong, being four square in shape, and of four hundred feet every way. On the north side is a gateway, and over the gate a tower very strongly fortified, wherein the Abbot is wont to keep prisoners such as offend in his jurisdiction.

Our daily manner of life is this. Soon after midnight the little bells are rung by the keeper of the church, and we assemble together for that service of God which is called matins. Matins being ended, we go back to our sleeping chamber. At six of the clock cometh the service of prime, to which we are called by the ringing of the smallest bell, time being given that we may put on our day habit and cleanse ourselves in the lavatory. And after prime is high mass without interval (this is a particular custom of the house, that the brethren may have the more time without interruption for study, or such work as may be laid upon them). Mass ended, there is given us a breakfast of bread and wine. Then follow study and work. And at eleven of the clock the cymbal is sounded that the brethren may wash their faces and hands at the conduit, and so make themselves ready for dinner. After this we go into the choir for sexts, where we sing together the Fifty-first Psalm and the Sixty-seventh, and thence to the burial-place, where we stand among the graves, our heads bare, that we may have them that are departed in perpetual recollection. After this, if it be the summer season, there is time allowed for sleep; and in winter they that will may walk. At three of the clock are nones, with study both before and after, and at five of the clock supper is served. After supper come vespers; and then, if the weather be fair, it is permitted to walk in the garden, or to play at bowls upon the green set apart and made smooth for that purpose. There are certain days of recreation when we may talk together, but on others such speech only is permitted as is needful. And four times in the year are the bathing days, and once in each month a day for shaving and clipping the hair.

Our habit is a black tunic, furred in winter; and over it an upper frock with great sleeves. On our heads we have a cowl, split, with pointed ends in front. In the winter season we have also a pelisse. Our boots are round toed, and not after the fashion commonly used, which maketh them long and pointed out of all reason, so that I have seen a gallant whose boot-ends did curl well-nigh up to his knees. Beneath we have for clothing a shirt of linsey-woolsey; our hosen are of white cloth, and our breeches tied with laces. Each man hath also a pouch wherein are a knife, a comb, a bodkin, needle and thread, and a writing tablet.

But the thing of which I am chiefly concerned to write is the *scriptorium*, which may be rendered the chamber for the writing and making of books; and herein I am constrained, by the love and honour which I do bear to his name, to make mention of one who did use this chamber in time past, to wit Matthew Paris, who, though he attained not to higher dignity than to be plain monk of this house, yet hath a name above that of any abbot that bath ruled it from the beginning until now.

This Matthew, then, surnamed of Paris, either because he was born in that city, or, as I rather think, because he was sometime a scholar of the University that is therein, took the monk's habit in the year of our Lord, 1217, being then seventeen years of age. King Henry, the third of the name, had him in great esteem, and commanded his presence on certain great occasions of state, to the end that these might find in him a worthy chronicler. Thus in the month of October, in the year 1247, he sent for him to be present at the feast of King Edward the Confessor, that was held at Westminster, and himself desired him to write an account of what had been done thereat. And when, in the space of three years afterwards, the king's daughter was married to Alexander of Scotland, Matthew of Paris was present at the marriage. And in the year 1257 the King came to the monastery and tarried there as a guest for a whole week, during which time he bade Matthew sit as a guest at his table, and held much talk with him in his chamber, telling him many things out of his own knowledge and experience wherewith he might enrich and enlarge his history. And when the University of Oxford was in danger to suffer from the encroachment of the Bishop of Lincoln, in whose diocese the said university is locally situate, the said Matthew prevailed with the King that the Bishop should not have his way. Nor was he held in less regard by them that bare rule in the house. So, when the House of the Benedictines at Drontheim in Norway, had fallen into no small trouble and confusion by reason of the ill-management of its abbots, this Matthew was sent thither that he might order things for the better, being held to be a prudent man and well skilled in affairs. But his fame chiefly resteth in the books that he wrote; that is to say, the *Greater Chronicles*, in which he recordeth the history of the world, from the Creation to the year of our Lord 1259 (in which same year he died); also the *History of the English*, which is, indeed, the said *Chronicles* writ short, and the *Lives of the Abbots of St. Alban's*. A very great and notable writer was he, a lover of his country, and one that set himself against all wrongdoing and tyranny, by whomsoever it might have been committed. And he was so skilful with his pen that he could not only write most eloquently therewith, but could also pourtray that concerning which he wrote, drawing faces of men, and battles, and councils, and divers other things, as may be seen to this day in sundry volumes yet preserved in this house.

This Matthew died, as I have said, in the year 1259, worn out by infirmity, though he had not attained to a great age. But he had laboured in his calling with diligence too great, not verily for his fame, but for his health and life. And, indeed, he had been constrained for some years before his death to use the help of others in the writing of his histories. There is yet to be seen the likeness of this Matthew, drawn after his decease, as he lay upon his bed in the infirmary, in the habit of a monk.

OF THE WRITING CHAMBER IN ST. ALBANS ABBEY

I WILL now speak more particularly of the *scriptorium*, wherein, by the favour of my lord Abbot, from my very first coming to the house, I have been suffered to abide. And for this I am most heartily thankful to him, and to my good father, now deceased, who taught me to write fairly, an art wherein he himself did excel, training my hand to the work while it was yet tender, and to my mother, who did first instruct me in drawing and the using of colours and gold. For I see that such brethren who are appointed to the work of the *scriptorium* are, for the most part, happier than their fellows, who, for want of that which shall fitly employ them, do suffer much discontent and weariness. For though there shall be one whom it sufficeth to spend his days in devout contemplation, and another who never wearieth of singing, and yet a third who can never have enough of reading and books, yet the greater part do crave some labour wherewith to occupy their days, and, for want of it, have many strifes one with another, or fall into evil ways, or are even overcome with madness. That some, indeed, are distraught by much learning, I know. Thus it was with Alexander of Langley, sometime a monk in this house, who, being learned above all his brethren, became wise in his own conceit. And when his pride and foolishness could no longer be endured, the brethren in chapter assembled visited him with their censure. Afterwards, when this availed nothing, John de Cella, being then Abbot, commanded that he should be beaten with stripes, even to much shedding of blood. And because his frenzy was yet unsubdued, he was carried to the cell of the house, which is at Bynham, in the county of Norfolk, and shut out from the sight of all men, and so continued till his death, being bound with chains, in which also he was buried. This I forget not; but, nevertheless, believe that more are distraught for lack of study or other occupation than for too great abundance thereof.

The *scriptorium* is a quiet chamber, with broad windows, very fairly glazed, so that there is no lack of light, and furnished with stools for sitting, and with desks conveniently ordered for writing. Twelve of the brethren do commonly labour therein, but, if there arise any urgent need, then can place be made for twenty. Such that have less skill and experience are set to the copying of letters and the like tasks—as, for example, when the Abbot will send a letter of greeting or concerning matters of business to the priors of the cells that belong to this house. To others is assigned the copying of books, wherein must be reckoned books for the service of the Church (for these, because of their much using, must needs be often renewed), and for the private study of the brethren, as commentaries and homilies and the like, books also of rhetoric and philosophy, the works of the Romans, and of the Greeks also (but these last rendered into Latin), not being forgotten. Of these books some are copied for our own using, and some that exchange may be made with other houses for such as we do not ourselves possess. Sometimes also we borrow the books of others for copying, first giving due security for their return.

To one brother is given the charge of the *scriptorium*. He assigneth to each his work, being himself under command of the Abbot, and seeth that it be done aright, and that no damage be suffered by any book. Also he keepeth a list of the books that go forth of the library with the names of those that borrow them. And twice or thrice in the year he revieweth all the books, that such as need restoring, whether from dampness, or from the devouring of the book-worm, or from natural decay of time, may receive due repair. Also he hath charge of the skins, be they of sheep or goats, on which the writing is to be made, and of the ink, taking due care that none be used but such as shall endure, and of the pens.

It is a law that silence should be kept in the *scriptorium*. Therefore, he that hath need of anything signifies the same by signs. If he require a book, he must stretch forth his hand, moving his fingers as though he turned the leaves. If the book be a missal, he must also make the sign of the cross; if it be the Gospels, then he will make the sign of the cross upon his forehead; if it be a Psalter, then he will place his hands upon his head as in the shape of a crown; and if he require the work of a heathen, then he will scratch the ear with the hand, after the manner of a dog, because the heathen are to be counted no better than dogs. (This custom I like not, holding that these also, according to their degree, have spoken by the Spirit of God.)

The time of working varieth according to the season, for it is not permitted to have either lamp or candle in the *scriptorium*, lest haply the books be damaged by oil or grease dropping thereon. It must be noted also that much hindrance is caused by the mists, which do oftentimes, and more especially in the winter season, prevail in these parts, so that for many days together the scribes will sit altogether idle, or work but for a small part of the day only.

I do gather from that which I have read concerning this matter that Abbot Paul, of Caen in Normandy, who came to the primacy of this house in the year of our Lord

1077, did first set apart a chamber for this work. And this he did, being prompted thereto by the liberality of a certain knight of Normandy, who gave to the house for this end certain tithes in Hatfield and Redbourn, which tithes are indeed so applied to this day. The said Abbot found not, as I understand, any brethren in the Abbey who had the needful skill, but was constrained to hire writers from without. But for many years now past there hath never failed from the brotherhood itself a sufficient supply of persons qualified for this work.

Nevertheless it must not be forgotten that many years before the coming of the said Paul of Caen, one Ælfric was wont to spend in the transcribing of books such time as the duties of his office of abbot might leave him.

Four years did I spend in the *scriptorium* with much content, during which time I did, by the ordering of the governor, give myself chiefly to the copying of ancient writers in the Latin tongue, for which work I was judged to be the more fit because I had pursued these studies with some applause at Oxford, it being well that the scribe should have a good understanding of that which he writeth. But that my soul should not suffer for want of spiritual food, I did make year by year one book of the Gospels or of the Psalter. But in the beginning of the fifth year, Brother Roger, that was illuminator, a man not old and, as one would judge, hale of body, was taken suddenly with sickness, and died within the space of one day. And it was doubted much who should be put into his place, but in the end I was chosen. From this choice I did gain no small advantage, not only from the nature of the work, than which there can be none more various or delightful, but because there is set apart for the illuminator a small chamber, of which he hath the sole use. And this he hath, not only that he may do his work in peace and quietness, but because he hath need of some convenient place where he may keep his colours, his washes of gold and silver, and other implements of his craft, and also—for this is no small matter—such things as serve him for the models of his painting. For I have ever, if I may say so much of my own handiwork, striven with all my might to picture such things as it fell to my lot to represent as truthfully and well as might be. If I had to make the presentment of any person, this I did according to my best conception of what he may have been, taking for my guidance, in outward matters of dress and the like, such mention as I could find in books. And as for trees and flowers, and birds and beasts, these I have to the best of my ability copied from the things themselves, if occasion served, or I could by any means procure them. Some, indeed, have I thus been able to picture from the life, as lilies and doves and sparrows, and the like common things. And once, when I had occasion to picture an eagle as being the sign of St. John the Evangelist, then, by great good fortune, came the forester of the Abbey, that had shot with his bow an eagle—that is no common bird in these parts. But in such things I have been for the most part content to follow the picturing of them who have before laboured in this place.

I cannot easily say in words how full of delight is this chamber to me, for though it doth not contain the greater treasures of the house, such as the missal bound in gold and the psalter incomparably illuminated with the same, which Abbot Geoffrey gave to the Brotherhood, yet it hath many precious volumes, to which I hope to add more than one of my own workmanship. Verily, though I have been buffeted with many waves, God hath brought me into safe haven at last. And now I will go on to write somewhat of my life in time past, especially of how, by the ordering of God, as indeed I cannot but believe, I was brought to this place. And that I be not tedious to any one whom it may please to read what I have here written, I will pass over such things as concern the time of my childhood, and come without loss of time to the year of my going to school.

OF MY SOJOURN AT ETON

ON the fourth day of September, in the year of our Lord 1450, I, having then ten years of age, was entered of the college of Eton, the which college King Henry, sixth of the name, had founded nine years before. I was the elder son of one William Aylmer, Serjeant-at-law, a learned man, as would be testified by others who speak without the partiality of a son, but of a small estate. He had been like to be made a judge of the realm in due course, being not learned only, but of such honesty as never was questioned in matters small or great (for, as Sallust hath it, while it is seen of some how vile they are even in a small matter of money, others are discovered only in some great thing). Courteous also was he, so that there were none that knew him but had a favour for him. But it pleased God that he should never have this promotion; for, being present at the trial of certain prisoners that had lain in the prison of Newgate for the space of six months and more, he was stricken with fever (as was also the judge and three officers of the court, and of the counsellors and attorneys twenty at the least) and died presently, being then scarce forty years of age. Five children did he leave orphans, three maids and two boy-children, of whom I was the elder. Now my mother, being of the family of Patten, was of the kindred of William of Waynflete, whom, in the year of our Lord 1443, king Henry did make Provost of Eton; and she, being sore burdened with the charge of her children, made application to the said William, being then Bishop of Winchester, for help in the rearing of them; and this he gave without grudging or delay, being of a most liberal temper, as is testified and proved, not only by his right noble and pious foundation of Magdalen College at Oxford, but also—for some that do great alms in public are mean and grudging in private matters—by many good deeds done secretly. To my mother he appointed a pension of thirty marks by the year, making it a charge on certain lands of his own; and this he did, not only as considering the frailty of human life and the uncertainty of mortal things, but because he would not that the revenue of a bishop should be burdened with any charge of his own kindred. And it is convenient that I here set down what this said most worthy bishop hath done for my own people. Joan, that was the eldest, he gave in marriage to one Thomas Bradgate, a counsellor learned in the law. The said Thomas had been wont in time past to learn of my father things that appertained to the study of the law, and when he was of age to plead in the courts had not ceased to consort with him as with one that was wiser than himself. And so it came to pass that he conceived a great love for my sister Joan, though indeed she was little more than a child. To him, therefore, was she given in marriage two years after the death of my father, the bishop aforesaid furnishing her with a dower of two hundred marks. The like liberality did he bestow upon my sister Margery, that was married, in the year next following, to one Philip Staples, that was a yeoman in the county of Worcester, and having a fair estate of three hundred acres, of which fifty were orchard, and rich beyond all other lands in the said county, as he was wont to affirm. My third sister, Alice, having a call to the religious life, was entered as a novice in the nunnery of Godstow, which is hard by the city of Oxford. Of her I shall have occasion to speak hereafter. My brother James, that was younger than I by two years, was bound apprentice to Master Kingsley, a mercer of the City of London, and hath married the said Kingsley's daughter, and is in all respects a prosperous citizen.

And now I will speak of myself. The said Bishop William procured me to be named one of the King's scholars in the college of Eton, the number of the said scholars being three-score and ten. Of these I was indeed the latest come, but not the youngest in years, for some had not more than eight years of age, nor the least advanced in learning. This last advantage I owed to the care of my father, who did not suffer himself to be hindered by any business of his own from teaching me. So it was that when I was admitted to the college of Eton I knew the accidence of the Latin tongue, so that I would scarce fail therein, and could read with understanding some of the easier portions of the Sorrows of Ovid, yea, and could make shift, with some help given, to put together a distich of Latin. And, indeed, there were not many so well furnished as I, at least of the younger sort, so that it came to pass that, whereas others of my years were put in charge of the usher, I was taught of the upper master. Nor was this only a help to me in my learning, but it did also set me free from certain servile tasks, as the cleaning of chambers, fetching of water, making of fires in the winter season, and the like, which did fall on such as were of lower place in the school. Verily I remember this time with much pleasure, and shall not count it lost labour if I do set down in order some of the things, both of earnest and of sport, which it was then our custom to do.

Our manner of life, then, was this. There were, as I have said, threescore scholars and ten; and, out of these, four were appointed to be *præpositi*, or "prepositors," as it may be writ in English. We did all sleep in one great chamber, and one of the said four prepositors had the charge of the chamber for a week, and, when the week was ended, another, and so till each had discharged his duty. In the morning, then, at five of the clock, the prepositor that had authority for the time cried with a thundering voice, "Surgite," that is to say, "Rise." Then we did rise altogether, for it fared ill with any that would ape the sluggard and seek a little more folding of the hands to sleep, and we put on our clothing, saying aloud meanwhile certain prayers. These being ended, each made his own bed, and swept under and about it, so that no dust or foulness should remain. And all that was so swept was gathered together in heaps, which heaps four of the scholars, appointed thereunto by the prepositor, would carry away to the appointed place. After this we went in order, walking two and two, to wash our hands. And our hands being washed, we entered into the school-chamber and took each his proper place. At six of the clock came in the usher and said certain prayers kneeling and heard such things as had been learned over night, according as time might serve, beginning with the lowest place. Meanwhile one of the prepositors wrote down the names of such as had been absent, if any there were, and gave them to the usher; and another scanned diligently the faces and hands of the younger sort, so that none should come to his tasks unwashen. And if he found any such, he wrote down their names and gave them to the upper master.

Our manner of learning was this. The master of the school would give forth in a loud voice certain sentences in the vulgar tongue. These sentences such as were of the fourth class would render into Latin, and such as were of the fifth would enlarge as their wits might prompt, and the sixth and seventh, being the highest in place, would arrange in order of verse. At other times he would read from a book, making choice of such passages as for easiness might best suit the capacity of them that he taught. And what he read his scholars would write down; and when they had got such an understanding of it as that they might, they would gather therefrom aught that was noteworthy—proverbs, to wit, or similitudes, or histories of notable places or persons, and the like. For the younger scholars the upper master would read the *Sorrows* of Ovid and Virgil's *Pastorals*, and for the elder Virgil's *Æneid* and the *Letters* of Cicero. At eleven of the clock we ate, though, indeed, the most took occasion to have something before. In the afternoon we did for the most part rehearse such things as we had learned in the morning. At six of the clock, I do remember, certain of the elder scholars that were set to this task by the masters did teach the younger. At seven of the clock we supped, and after this, permission having been given, played awhile, and so to bed.

On Friday there was inquisition had of such as had done amiss during the week past, that they might suffer due punishment. To these, verily, it was a day of dread, for Rhadamanthus himself, whom the ancients did feign to be the judge of the dead, was not more stern than the upper master, who, though he chastised not the guilty with the snakes of the Furies, yet did with his birch rods exact full penalty of guilt. But to them that had acquitted themselves well, it was a day to be highly esteemed, seeing that our tasks were lightened.

At certain seasons also of the year there was given to us some indulgence. Thus, on the Feast of the Conversion of St. Paul (being the twenty-fifth day of the month of January), or on some other day at that season, as the weather and other occasions might serve, we went to a certain place named the Mount. There did we take all scholars that had been added to the foundation during the year last past, whom, having first sprinkled with salt, we did afterwards handle with such wit (which in the Latin tongue is *sal*, salt) as we could command. And it was permitted to us to say what we would, so only it was said in Latin, and had a certain elegance, and lacked scurrility. Yet I doubt me much whether the thing was pleasing to the said new corners, who did oftentimes add yet another kind of salt, shedding salt tears. And at one of the clock we returned to the college and played till the hour of sleep.

Also on the first day of May, those that would might rise at four of the clock and gather boughs of hawthorn wherewith to adorn the windows of the chamber, provided only that they did not come thereinto with feet wetted or muddied.

Also in September, on some day that the master did appoint, we would go into the woods to gather nuts, which we did with great mirth and jollity. But first it was demanded of us that we should make verses in the Latin tongue, praising the fertility of autumn.

Also in November, on the day of St. Hugh, sometime Bishop of Lincoln, we chose a boy bishop, who did hold a visitation, and pass censure on such as seemed to have offended against the scholars in the year past; yea, and performed also a certain semblance of the mass. Writing this I am minded of another custom touching holy things that seemeth worthy of note, namely, that on the night of Easter Eve three or four of the elder scholars, chosen by the master, at the asking of him that had charge of the chapel, watched with candles of wax and torches, as though they watched at the tomb of the Lord, lest the Jews should steal the body.

At Christmas-tide we had also much mirth and sport. And once in the year we were suffered to depart to our homes, or, if the said homes were too far distant, to the houses of such friends as were willing to receive us. This licence was given to us on the Feast of the Ascension; only a charge was laid on us that we should return to the college on the eve of the Feast of Corpus Christi. Such as came not back at the appointed hour were beaten with rods of birch; but if any were absent yet longer, their place in the college was altogether taken from them. So it came to pass that, if Easter fell as early as it may, we had near upon three weeks of holiday; but if, on the other hand, it fell at latest—that is to say, on the twenty-sixth day of April—we had none.

Many things might I write concerning my sojourn in this said school of Eton: how we did swim in the Thames, which is here a right noble and beautiful stream, also how we did angle therein, and catch no small abundance of trout and other fishes; for indeed there is no river in all Christendom, as I have heard say, that hath greater plenty of fish than Thames. And indeed I mind me to this day of a certain great trout that had ten pounds and a half of weight, which I did catch by the mill of Master Roger at Windsor. For an hour and more was I striving with the monster, which had well-nigh drawn me into the water, as the holy youth Tobit was well-nigh drawn. Once also I verily thought he had escaped me, having wound my angling line round a perilous great post that is the mill-tail. Yet at the last, to my great joy, I handled him, Master Miller helping with a net, for he loved ever that the scholars should take their pleasure in angling, so that they first asked his grace. This great fish did I give to the upper master, deeming that it could not worthily be served at a less honourable table; and he called me and four other of the scholars with me to supper. And he gave us a flask, yea, if my memory serveth, two flasks, of Malmsey wine; and we had much pleasant talk with him, sitting at table till ten of the clock, for it was the Feast of St. John at the Latin Gate, when a certain licence beyond the usual is allowed. Verily, as the poet hath it, "these things it delighteth me to remember," only I may not spend too much time upon them, having weightier matters whereof to write.

Yet is there one other thing that I must needs tell. In the month of March, in the year 1452, I, with some seven or eight other of the scholars, did enter into the garden of the King's castle at Windsor. And this we were suffered to do, for the King, having a great kindness for his scholars of Eton, would have it so; only it was laid upon us a charge that we should not thrust ourselves into such places as the King himself was wont to frequent. Now, whether we had forgotten this charge, as indeed as boys are apt to forget, or whether the King had wandered beyond the walks wherein he was wont to keep himself, I know not; but so it fell that we came upon him unawares, while he stood looking into a little pool that there is in the garden. There was no one in his company save one little page boy of ten years or thereabouts. Nor had he any of the state of a king. On his head he had a plain cap of blue velvet, very dark of hue, without feather or jewel or badge. His doublet was of black silk, and his mantle of silk also, dark blue, and his hosen black. Nor did he carry any sword or dagger in his girdle; but he had a book in his hand. Now, when we came upon him, and this, as I have written, we did unawares, turning a corner suddenly, we made as though we would have fled, but he beckoned to us that we should stay. And when we had made our obeisance he talked with us, questioning us of our books, yea, and of our sports also. And when he had ended his questioning he said as to himself, in a low voice, but so that we heard him, "Happy ye that are simple scholars, and have not laid upon you this grievous charge of a crown;" and after, in a louder voice, "Be ye good boys, be gentle and tractable and servants of the Lord." Then he gave to each one of us a quarter-mark, and bade us God-speed. A comely face he had, but of a woman rather than a man; and his regard was sad, and at times, methought, did wander somewhat; and indeed, not many weeks after, he was for a time distraught. Verily, if I may say so much without arraigning of Him that doth order all things, he was ill set upon a throne. He had done better as a monk, for he loved books and learning and quiet ways. Also he was a lover of God, and walked purely and discreetly all his days; but to deal with affairs of state, and to lead armies, and to keep the peace between turbulent men that sought each his own advantage—these things he could not do. And so it fell out that though there never sat on this throne of England a more pious and godly prince, yet never hath there been King under whom the realm hath suffered more grievous loss and damage. I pray that God lay not this evil to his charge, but rather reckon to him that he ever loved learning and virtue and true religion.

HOW I GO TO OXFORD

IN the month of September, in the year 1455, the Lord Bishop of Winchester, my good friend and patron, cometh to Eton; who, after talk had with the Provost and Master, sendeth for me. And when I was come into his presence, and had made him due obeisance, louting on one knee, and kissing his hand, and he, on his part, had kissed me on either cheek, he saith, "Nephew Thomas "—for he would call me nephew, though I was not, indeed, nearer of kin to him than cousin in the second degree—"Nephew Thomas, I hear a good report of thee from thy teachers, that thou hast made such progress in honest letters, that there remaineth not much in this place for thee to learn. Wilt thou, then, be a scholar of Oxford? I have it in my mind to set up there a college for the encouragement of true religion and sound learning, and, indeed, have already made some beginning towards the executing of this purpose. Also I have thereto the consent and favour of my lord the King, who, though he would willingly have persuaded me to build my college at Cambridge, where he hath set his foundation of King's College, yet hath approved my design. For when I set forth to him how I would convert St. John Baptist Hospital, which King Henry, his father, did found, into a college, he made answer, 'Well, Master William, if it be so in good deed, I am glad to hear of your godly intentions. What assistance in this matter you would that I should do, Master William, I will forthwith do it.' I have for the present, therefore, set up a hall, which I have called the Hall of St. Mary Magdalen, and have put therein a president and scholars. Now, Master Provost here telleth me that there is like to be no vacant place in King's College for some time to come. If so be, then, that thou desirest to advance thy studies further, I will make thee of this said Magdalen Hall, not forgetting to give thee such sustenance as thou mayest need. And when my college is founded, which, indeed, I hope will be, God favouring, within the space of twelve months at the most, I will take thee thither, and put thee in a scholar's place. And verily, so only God help me, thou shalt not be ashamed of thy college, Nephew Thomas." And, indeed, already at the date of this writing, though the work be not yet altogether finished, there is no fairer foundation in all Christendom, whether you regard the nobility of the buildings, or the greatness of the revenues, or the number and learning of the fellows and scholars that are nurtured therein. I pray that it may ever have this pre-eminence, and that it be not corrupted by riches, as hath befallen other foundations, wherein the very liberality of benefactors hath turned to the undoing of their work.

Thereafter the good Bishop spake to me concerning my future life; how should I behave myself at Oxford. He warned me that I should not consort with men of violence, or with them that give themselves overmuch to sport, and that I should not mix myself with the strifes that are between the diverse nations of scholars on the one hand, and between the whole body of scholars and the townsfolk on the other. "Be reverent," he said, "to thy elders and betters; fail not to uncover thy head to any that is of a master's degree; be not abroad from thy chamber after eight of the clock at the latest, except for grave cause; and apply thyself diligently to thy learning. Thou hast now a few years for seed-time (which will pass but too quickly, though now they seem long in the looking forward), but the harvest shall be for all thy life." And other words he spake—not many, but weighty—concerning faith and morals, which, indeed, I keep in my heart, remembering them as though they were spoken but yesterday, but will not set down in this place, because they were for my private ear only.

His admonition ended, the Bishop took from his pouch five marks, and gave them to me, saying, "Thy lodging, and thy meat and drink, with lights and such other things as thou needest, will be furnished thee without spending of thine. But thou must buy the furniture of thy chamber from him that had it before thee; and thou wilt also be at some cost for thy journey. And I would that thou shouldst have something of money in thy pouch for such needs as may occur, and especially for almsgiving. Be not over careful, nor over ready to spend. But fear not to spend upon books, so only thou buy them for the goodness of their matter, and not for the show of their binding, or the bravery of gold and colours. In this I will bear thee out, so that thou goest not beyond reason in thy purchasing. Look not for an inheritance from me, Nephew Thomas, for of that which is my own I have made other disposal, and that which cometh from the Church, to the Church it shall go back; but I will not spare to furnish thee well for that station of life to which thou shalt be called." Then the Bishop, having first given me his blessing, departed.

On the fifth day of October there cometh to the college one Robert Westby, a fetcher of scholars to and fro the University of Oxford, having turned aside somewhat from his way by request of the Provost that he might take me in his company. Master Westby had in his train twenty scholars or thereabouts, whom he had gathered from divers places in the county of Kent, to which county he belongeth by birth, being a citizen of Canterbury, and, when he is not busied with the fetching of scholars, a scrivener by occupation. Certain of these twenty were of tender age, having not more than twelve years; and there was one only that was of like age with myself. On the morrow we set out, and that day we rode to Henley-upon-Thames, and lay at a certain hostelry that is hard by the river, having the sign of the Swan. A fair town and a clean is this same Henley, and Thames here is yet broader and fairer to behold than he is at Eton. We had a sweet lodging at the said inn, and a supper of flesh and bread and eggs and beer. And Master Brakespear, that was mayor of the town, a lover of learning and a kinsman of Nicholas Brakespear that was Pope under the title of Adrian IV, sent two flasks of Malmsey for our better entertainment. I mind me that of these flasks

Master Westby gave one cup to me and one to my companion of like age, and took the rest for himself, deeming it better, I doubt not, that the younger scholars should not be touched over soon with a liking for strong drink, of which liking he himself did know how full of damage it is. The next day we rose at six of the clock, and came before evening to Oxford, having rested awhile at Watlington, which lieth half-way between Oxford and Henley. And so, having first passed by a ford over a certain small stream that is called Cherwell, we came to the city gate, and, this being passed, to Magdalen Hall, whither I was bound, the said hall standing at a furlong's length or thereabouts from the river upon the left-hand side of the way.

Here I parted from Master Westby, and paid him his charges—to wit, for my supper at Henley, two pence; and to my dinner at Watlington, two pence; and to the hire of my horse and his food, four pence.

This done, I was taken by the porter to Master Horneley, Bachelor of Divinity, being the President of the said hall, who, having been advised beforehand of my coming by letter from the Bishop, wherein I was spoken of, it would appear, with praise beyond my deserts, received me with much courtesy and favour. Saith he, Master Aylmer, I have a fair chamber for you, which indeed I would not give but to one that will do credit to the house: and this, as my good lord the Bishop hath written, thou art like to do. It looketh towards the south, and this is of no small advantage, for the saving of fuel in the winter season, so that thou wilt find thine allowance suffice. And in summer it is not ever hot, because it is not close under the roof. It hath been built this hundred years and more, yet never hath any scholar that dwelt therein died of plague or fever." Therewith he taketh me to a chamber that was some fourteen feet each way, and having nine feet of height. Two windows it had, fairly glazed. It was, I take it, not less than thirty feet from the ground.

After this the President taketh from his pouch a bill of the goods and chattels of him that had of late dwelt in this chamber. This bill I have kept, and will here set forth:

1 Bed	16d.
1 Mattress	20d.
2 Blankets	16d.
1 Coverlet with birds and flowers	16d.
4 Sheets	8d.
1 Coffer	2d.
4 Candlesticks	10d.
3 Chairs	3d.
1 Curtain for the bed of white . . .	2d.
2 Curtains for the windows of red	6d.
1 Lantern	2d.
1 Table	8d.
1 Bellows for the fire	1d.
3 Plates, 2 cups, 3 knives, 3 forks	15d.

The sum of these things was one hundred and twenty-five pence, that is to say, thirty-five pence short of one mark. Also there was a hornpipe which was valued at the price of one penny; but this I sold to a certain townsman that dealt in such things for the same money, and therefore count it not in my furnishing. But I find not in this bill aught for towels. Of these I bought three, paying therefore six pence, and four pence I paid to the writer of the bill. Also on the morrow I bought a pen and an inkhorn and paper, for the which I paid one shilling. And that which was left out of the mark, being five pence (for the cost of travelling was eight pence) I gave in alms to the poor, that there might be a blessing on my work, for as the Scripture hath it, "Qui dat pauperibus is mutuatur Domino." That which remained to me of the Bishop's money I gave in charge to Master Thomas, the Manciple, keeping only therefrom for present needs one shilling. For it was my purpose to take counsel of my teachers touching the buying of books.

OF MY SOJOURN AT OXFORD AND OF JOHN ELIOT

SO much have I said of my leaving the College of Eton and coming to Oxford, and of my settling myself in a chamber in Magdalen Hall. And now I will write somewhat of my manner of life. And first of outward things. For my chamber I paid three shillings and sixpence by the term, and for my commons, that is to say, for food and drink, twelve pence by the week; for lectures I paid two shillings by the term; and of terms there are four in the year. Also to the servants of the hall, of whom there were twain, the upper and the lower, one shilling and four pence by the year. Now these things being added together, and forty weeks being reckoned unto the year, it followeth that I was at a cost year by year of fifty-three shillings and four pence. Now the Bishop did make to his scholars an allowance, till his college should have its revenues duly appointed supplied, of three pounds by the year. And to me he gave, by the hands of the Principal, twenty shillings further for kindred's sake, as he said. And he was ready also to provide so much more as should be needed from time to time upon occasions extraordinary, such as the taking of the degree, when a scholar must give a feast to the masters that examine him, and also give them robes or other gifts.

On the feast of St. Benet, being the ninth day of October and the first of Michaelmas term, High Mass was said at the Church of St. Mary, and after a sermon was preached in the Latin tongue, wherein we scholars were warned, or such of us at the least as could understand the words spoken, that we should fear God and be obedient unto our governors. On the morrow, and on all the days following, except, indeed, it was a festival, I heard a lecture from the President at nine of the clock, and another in the schools at ten in rhetoric, and yet another in logic at twelve. And after dinner there were lectures again, or disputations of those that disputed for their degrees, from one of the clock till three. These exercises being ended, I would walk abroad in the fields for my recreation, or sometimes would play at ball with my fellows, or stand and watch when certain of the higher sort of scholars (for to none others was it permitted) would contend together at tennis. And sometimes there was a match of shooting at a mark with the long-bow or the cross-bow, and at other times there would be leaping and wrestling. These all I liked well to see, but took no part therein, having loved quieter ways from my youth.

And now to tell of certain things that came to pass while I dwelt at Oxford. I do remember that on the morrow of All Souls, in the first year of my sojourn, while I sat in the School of Logic, about half-past ten of the clock there came a great knocking at the door, which when one of the scholars had opened, appeareth thereat the Bedell, crying with a loud voice, "Master Willoughby," for he it was that lectured, "hast thou here one John Weston?" Now the said Weston sat by me, and when he heard his name, he rose up in his place, and said, "What seekest thou of me, Master Bedell?" And he answered, "I have authority to take thee before the Chancellor, or his deputy, for that thou didst draw thy dagger upon William the Tailor, in St. Ebbe's, at four of the clock in the afternoon on the feast of All Saints." Then all the scholars that sat in the chamber rose up and followed the Bedell and Master Weston to Lincoln College, whereof the Rector, Doctor John Beke, was deputy for the Chancellor. And as we went I heard not a little whispering and murmuring from certain friends and companions of the said Weston. Thus one did say, "This William the Tailor is a sorry villain, and it had been no loss, but rather a gain, if Weston had slain him. He did take half a mark of me for a doublet and cloak of blue cloth but six months since, and the doublet hath holes already." "Yea," said another, "he played me a like scurvy trick; and when I was loth to pay, haled me before the Chancellor and so compelled me." Then said a third, "Shall we take him out of the hands of the Bedell?" "Nay," answered one that seemed older and of greater authority, "that were ill done. See, there be six stout fellows with arms that are ready to help the Bedell, so that it is most like ye will harm yourselves and do no good to Master Weston." And when we came to Lincoln College, which is a fair building but unfinished, the greater part tarried without; but two or three friends went with Master Weston before the deputy. These, coming forth in no long space, said that the deputy had bound him to keep the peace towards William the Tailor, and put upon him a fine of four shillings, and that he should be imprisoned in the Castle of Oxford till the said fine should be paid. "And there will he lie," saith one, "for he hath not four shillings—no, nor the half of it." "Nay," the other made answer, "we will order it better than that. For, though he hath not money, he hath that whereof money may be made." And when I inquired of one that stood by what these words meant, he answered, "Come, if thou wouldst know—for I perceive that thou art new to this place—to the Church of St. Mary the Virgin, on the Feast of St. Andrew, at nine of the clock; for Master Weston must even lie in prison for so long." So on the Feast of St. Andrew I went to the said church. Hard by the screen of the altar was a great chest, bound with iron, and having on the lid a great lock. And there stood by the chest two priests wearing gowns, and over their gowns black capes, and over the capes hoods of white fur. "These," said he that had spoken to me, for he also had come, "be the keepers of the chest, and one is, of the northern nation and one of the southern. And he that hath the hood of red is the Bursar of Lincoln College, who is also joined in the trust." "But," said I, "what meaneth this chest?" And he laughed, but softly and under his breath, as remembering in what place he stood, and made answer, "Happy thou, young sir, if thou shouldst never have occasion to know. But hearken. This is the chest of William Audley, Bishop of Lincoln. He left therewith one hundred marks to the end that such scholars of this University that had need might borrow on pledges. These pledges are kept in the chest, and this day is appointed for the redeeming of them, and for lending the money afresh. And he that standeth by, with an ink horn and a pen in his girdle, is Master More, the stationer, whose charge it is that a pledge be rightly appraised, and that the chest suffer no loss. But note what shall be done." Then I saw that one of the two keepers put his key into the lock and turned it, and then the other, and after him, again, the Bursar of Lincoln College. And when the three keys had been so turned, the lock was opened. After this there came not a few, both masters and bachelors and scholars, with money in their hands wherewith to redeem their pledges. The pledges were for the most part books; but I noted also sundry cups, and daggers with hilts of silver. And when all had come and departed, having paid their money, and taken that which they sought, there yet remained five or six pledges that were not redeemed. "These," said my companion, "will be presently sold; only Master More will not suffer that they should be sold for less than their true worth. But note, my friend, that the cups and daggers are redeemed all of them, but the pledges that are left are books. 'Tis ever so, for men love feasting and fighting better than learning." Nevertheless, when the books were sold there lacked not purchasers. After this the money was counted. And I saw that the two keepers differed from each other in the counting, which they did, not once or twice only, but many times. But at the last the Bursar of Lincoln, who, they say, is a notable man in such matters, did put the matter right. After this followed the lending out of money upon pledges. First cometh the

Bursar of Brasenose College that would borrow sixty shillings (for more may not be lent upon pledges) upon a missal, very fairly bound in white vellum and gold, and with rare pictures within, as I saw, when he showed the book to Master More. And after him certain masters with books and cups and the like. And after the masters the bachelors, and after the bachelors the scholars. Of these last, one would fain have borrowed certain moneys upon a cross-bow, to whom one of the keepers spake roughly, "Nay, Sirrah, we lend not the Bishop's money on such goods as thine. And what hast thou to do with cross-bows and such gear? Knowest thou not that it is not lawful for scholars to carry arms? 'Tis well for thee that there is no Proctor at hand, else wouldst thou lose it altogether and suffer a fine also." Then the poor lad turned away, not without tears, though these he was fain to hide. And I had knowledge of him that he had sat nigh me many times when Master Williams lectured on rhetoric, and that he was ill-clad and as, I judged, ill-fed, but of a keen wit, if ever wit can be seen in a man's countenance, and most intent upon learning. After him cometh up Master Weston's friend with a dagger, having a silver hilt in his hand. "I would borrow six shillings upon this," saith he. "Nay," said the keeper, when he had talked awhile with Master More, "thou canst have but four only." "Ye are over-hard," saith the scholar, "for this is a true blade of Damascus, and the silver is of the best, and the workmanship of no mean skill. Also there is a jewel of amethyst in the upper part of no small worth. Moreover it is the chattel of a poor scholar that must lie in a prison except he can pay his fine." "I care not for thy poor scholar," saith Master Keeper, "for whom doubtless prison is the fittest place. But I will look again at the dagger, Didst see the amethyst, Master More?" "'Tis no great matter," said he, "yet ye may lend five shillings and sixpence more without damage to the chest." And this was done. Then, for there were none other pledges to be dealt with, the chest was locked again with the three keys, and the people departed from the church.

But as I went back to the hall I was aware of the poor scholar with the cross-bow. And God, for I doubt not that it was He, put it into my heart that I should speak to him. So I said, "I pray thy pardon that I should speak, being a stranger, but I have seen thee in Master Williams his logic lecture, and I would fain help thee, for thou seemest to be in trouble." "I thank thee," answered he, "for thy good will; but my trouble is past thy help." And he made as if he would turn away. But I, though I be not by nature bold and confident with strangers, would not leave him, for something within me seemed to forbid; and, at the last, after much insistency on my part, he told me his story. "I am," said he, "a yeoman's son at Peckwater Hall. And because I was a lover of books from the very first, my father sent me to this place. But he has had a hard shift to keep me here, for the farm is but poor land, and there are three of us besides myself—that is to say, three sons and two daughters. And now things go the worse with us by reason of the wars. This week he had thought to send me ten shillings; but the soldiers came forth out of Shrewsbury town and took a flock of geese, forty in all, fat birds, which he had ready for the market, so that he could send me nought. And now I owe to the Principal four shillings and ten pence for commons, though I live as sparely as I can, for I have not paid aught since the beginning of this term. And if I discharge not the debt, or at the least pay somewhat, I must depart, for such goods as I possess are but of little worth. And if I depart, then is all my time and labour lost, and I have been in this place for six years and more. Nor can I dig or follow the plough. Only one thing remaineth. The sword hath never enough to devour, and I will make my living out of that which hath brought me to ruin." Then I thought to myself that I should not ill spend good Bishop William's money if I helped this poor scholar. And this, that I dwell not over-long on my own doing, I did, lending him ten shillings. After he became my fast friend; and though through this friendship I did suffer, as I shall tell hereafter, if my strength suffice, such grievous sorrow as had like to bring me to the grave, never have I repented thereof; yea, and to this hour I love John Eliot—for that was the poor scholar's name—with my whole soul, and I do thank God who put it into my heart to help him.

OF THE COLLEGE OF ST. MARY MAGDELEN

ON the Feast of St. Mary Magdalen, in the year 1456, the Lord Bishop of Winchester did by God's blessing and favour fulfil the purpose which was in his heart, founding his college, which he named after the said saint, to whose honour he had ever a most special devotion. Let no one, indeed, think that he has at this time altogether finished the said college. Verily, at this present writing much yet remaineth to be done. Nevertheless, he at this time made a beginning, yea, and such a beginning as would have contented one of a less princely heart for an end. For on the feast day aforesaid there were finished for use lodgings for the President of the said college, and chambers for certain of the fellows and demies (for he called the scholars demies as having half commons). Also, there were built such necessary things as a kitchen and a buttery. But the chapel and the hall were not yet finished. For the Bishop was minded that these should be of such an excellence as should not be surpassed in any college of Christendom. And for the sustentation of this said college he had given sundry manors. Certain benefices also had he given, that when they that taught therein had fulfilled a certain number of years they might for greater ease and rest—for the Bishop knew how much toil and trouble they have who teach—be presented to the said benefices. Now the order of the doings on this day were as I shall now write.

First, there was the singing of High Mass in the Church of St. Mary the Virgin, at which many were present, and not a few notable persons—bishops, and abbots, and nobles, and the Chancellor, George Nevill, of Balliol College, and the principals of all the colleges, being seven in number, for the Rector of Lincoln College, Master Beck, came not, being hindered by the sickness of which not long after he died. Mass having been sung, the Bishop cometh to the Hall of St. Mary Magdalen, which was indeed to the college of the like name even as in the Commonwealth of the Jews the tabernacle was to the temple. In the said hall were gathered together the President and masters and scholars, and all others that did partake of the Bishop's bounty. And all the place about, even to the housetops, was crowded with an innumerable company of spectators. Then the Bishop leadeth across to the college the whole company of masters and scholars, the people making a great shouting, and not a few praying to God that He would bless this great work. Even as in old time some man of renown would lead a colony from a city whose borders were too strait for its inhabitants, so did the Bishop lead his company. And verily, as such founders of colonies were ever held in especial honour throughout all generations, so shall the Bishop be held in honour by all that enjoy his benefactions in time to come; yea, and by all Christian men. Truly, the lines have fallen in pleasant places to them that have a part in this college. For, not to speak of the beauty and conveniency of the buildings, the place itself is by nature delightsome. Here Cherwell floweth with a clear stream, bordered with fair trees; and there is a park of deer, such as a baron or earl might gladly possess. And when the Bishop, the President and masters and scholars following him, had compassed the whole domain, he gathered the whole company together under a great tree that there was, they of the college standing nighest to him, and the rest—that is to say, all the notable persons both in the University and in the city of Oxford—being without, and made an oration, of which

I will here set clown the substance. "Ye see here the beginning of a work which I have purposed to do for the glory of God, and for the commemoration of the Blessed Saint Mary Magdalen, and for the setting forward of religion and sound learning in this University and realm. And now, not for the glorifying of myself, but for the more effectual carrying out of my purpose, I will declare what is in my heart to do. I will that there be a President and Fellows of this college, the said Fellows being forty in number, priests all of them, but given to various studies such as are commonly followed in this place; and because there hath been talk elsewhere of favour and partiality in the choosing of fellows, I will that these be taken from various shires and dioceses in this realm as shall be ordered hereafter. And there shall be thirty scholars who shall be called demies. And for the more decent performance of divine, service there shall be chaplains skilled in singing, also singing men and singing boys, and for the teaching of the said boys and of others dwelling in this town, a schoolmaster and an usher. And I do lay a charge on all that are now or shall be hereafter partakers of this benefaction that they use such good things as shall be provided soberly and in the fear of God, and for the promoting of true religion and sound learning. And because the frailty of man is such that he needeth overseeing, I have ordained that the Bishop of Winchester shall be visitor of this college, with power to correct all disorders and abuses, so only that he change not the statutes that are made for its good government." This oration ended, the Bishop took from the hands of his notary sundry parchments and gave them to the President. "Here," said he, "ye have the titles of sundry manors and benefices which I have given, even as God hath given them to me, for your sustentation. Take heed that ye waste them not." After this the notary read aloud the charter under the hand of the King, whereby the President, fellows, and demies of the College of St. Mary Magdalen were made a Corporation with power to hold lands. And this done, the Bishop gave to the President a seal, saying, "Ye shall use this seal when ye shall have occasion to make any deed."

After this we went to the Church of St. Mary the Virgin, the chapel of the hall being too strait for the company, where the clerks sang the *Te Deum Laudamus*. This ended, it being now one of the clock, there was a great feast held. Of this I have kept the bill, and will here set it forth, knowing that such matters, though they are but of little moment to them that read at this present, will seem notable to them that come after. For do we not ourselves read with much pleasure how the ancients did eat and drink, at what price they did buy flesh and fish and wine, and many other matters of the same kind?

First. Brawn and mustard, with Malmsey.

FIRST COURSE.

A subtlety of St. George (that is to say, a figure of St. George slaying the Dragon done in sugar and wax).

Soup of meat of Cyprus.

Partridge in Red sauce.

Pestles of Venison roast.

Swan roast.

Fatted Capons.

Teals roast.

Pike salted.

Woodcocks baked.

Partridge in jelly.

A Dolphin in paste, a subtlety.

A Hart, a subtlety.

FIRST COURSE.

Crane roast.

Cony roast.

Heronshaw roast.

Curlewe roast.

Bream.

Venison baked.

A Dragon, a subtlety.

Jelly of Damascus.

Samson, a subtlety.

FIRST COURSE.

Dates in paste.

Peacock with his beak gilt.

Rabbits roast.

Partridges roast.

Plovers and Quails roast.

Larks roast.

Tench in jelly.

Venison baked.

Marchpane of filberts, pine nuts, pistachios, almonds, and rosed sugar.

Also Wafers and Hippocras when dinner was done.

Dinner ended, the Bishop drank to the President, and after gave him the cup out of the which he drank, a fair goblet of silver gilt, having three handles, which might hold three quarts at the least, saying, "This shall be thy cup, Master President, and of them that shall sit after thee in thy place." And the Chancellor drank to the Bishop. After this the company rose up and went each man to his own place.

The same day, after evensong, which the Bishop did sing himself, for he is not one who will do all such things by his chaplain, the Bishop sendeth for me, and, after he had questioned me of my welfare and of my studies, putting to me sundry questions in logic and philosophy which, by the favour of the Saints, I answered not amiss, he said, "Thy elders speak well of thee, Nephew Thomas. Now, as this is a day of benefactions, ask what thou wilt; and if it be within reason, as I doubt not it will, it shall be done unto thee." Then I bethought me of John Eliot, and that haply I might further his fortunes. So I set forth to the Bishop his poor estate and his great love of learning, saying at the last, "One hath helped him that he is not in any present need; but I doubt me much how it shall fare with him in the time to come; for he came to this place, he telleth me, but ill-taught, and can scarce answer for his degree for three years." Then said the Bishop, "And who is it that helped him? Nay, answer not, for thy blush betrayeth thee. Thou shalt have thy desire. I must needs ask, if it be but for form's sake, of the Principal of Peckwater, what manner of life he hath followed. And if, as I doubt not, the report be good, thy friend shall have a demy's place in the college." And this, that I be not tedious, was done the day following. After this the friendship that was between us two grew yet stronger and closer, seeing that we had not only as before oneness of temper, but also oneness of place.

OF MY FRIENDSHIP WITH JOHN ELIOT

I DOUBT me much whether there be anywhere in the world friendship so fast and so little marred by strife or jealousy or any such thing as that which doth sometimes spring up between young men that, being under the roof of one college, do follow in company both study and sport. Nor is it of necessity for such friendship that the two should be altogether like in temper and liking and manner of life. Thus there was between John Eliot and me something of difference, notably in this that he was of a fiercer temper and was over-ready with his hands when there was any occasion of strife. Very stalwart was he and strong, standing, like Saul the son of Kish, by head and shoulders above the people, for he had six feet and inches as many of stature, and a mighty boxer withal, having both strength and skill, so that I was wont to say not Castor himself, whom the ancients fabled to be prince of boxers, could have surpassed him. Now there were in the days of which I write such strifes and disputings, yea and such riots and tumults, as had scarce before been known since King Alfred of pious memory first did erect his University at Oxford. The place is always somewhat unquiet, ay and always will be, so long as the blood of youth shall be hot. But now not only were there the accustomed feuds, the Northern men contending with the Southern men, and the Welshmen, of whom there were many in the University, with the English, but the strife which was even then beginning to divide this whole realm, if I may so speak, into two armies did rage furiously, some following the House of York and some the House of Lancaster, so that not only were colleges divided against colleges, but often times a college would be divided against itself. Verily I have seen blood flowing and heads broken, and battles that but for the intervening of the older and wiser sort had ended in death, in the very quadrangle and hall of our college.

I do remember that there was a great fight between the scholars of Peckwater Hall and the scholars of Merton College, which fell out, if my memory serveth me well, after dark in the month of November. Of this, indeed, the first cause and beginning was no great matter, but a thing altogether mean and trifling. For nation did not rise against nation, nor they that favoured the white rose contend with them that loved rather the red; but a certain scholar of Merton did in a frolic snatch a can of beer which a citizen was carrying to his home. Of this a scholar of Peckwater, being his acquaintance that was robbed of the beer, took note. And so both parties crying "Rescue," there was within a short space of time a mighty uproar; and this all the more because it chanced to be a feast-day, and the hearts of some were lifted up within them with strong drink. For first the men of Merton drave back the men of Peckwater to their gate, so that they were fain to shut themselves within it. Then again these, having gathered their strength together, issued forth, and, taking their adversaries unaware, put them to flight, being not a little helped therein by the strong arm of John Eliot. For it so chanced that he and I had that day walked abroad, it being, as I have written, a holiday, and were now returning later than was our wont. So as we came up the street which is called High Street, returning towards our college from the village of Cumnor, we heard a great shouting. And when John Eliot discerned in this, for there was indeed a very Babel of voices, the cry "Peckwater," nothing would content him but he take his part in the fray, having been, as I have written before, at the first a scholar of this said hall. So he ran down the lane that is called Oriel Lane, I following him, for though I loved not his more turbulent mood; I would not leave him. And when we came to the space that is between Peckwater and Merton it was a very field of battle, into which straightway plungeth Master John, having no arms but those which nature provideth—for so far he was law abiding—but using these with all his might. And in a short space he came to the gate of Merton, which was now open to receive them that fled, and he would fain—so carried away was he by the fury of battle—have entered therein, even as Turnus in Virgil's "Æneid" entereth alone into the camp of Trojans, but that I caught him by the doublet, and besought him that he would take heed. "For this," I said, "is no quarrel of thine; and they that meddle with strife that concerneth them not will verily repent them of their foolishness. Think too," I said, "of the good Bishop, thy patron." When he heard this he held his hand, and stood aside from the fray. Thereupon the men of Merton recovered their ground, even as did the Trojans when Achilles came no longer into the battle. Then I said, "Shall we not depart, for surely they that make so great an uproar will answer for it." Nor did he refuse to listen to me. So we departed, very much to our profit, for we had scarce gone when came the Southern Proctor with his company and ran between the combatants to part them. But they, so eager were they for the battle, took no heed of him, yea and wounded him, smiting him with a stone upon the cheek so that his jaw was well-nigh broken, and with a staff upon the right arm so that he could not use it for the space of three months. After this came a great posse of masters whom the Chancellor's deputies had gathered together with the constables of the town and laid hands upon all whom they found. On every one of these, and also on all whom by inquisition held they could learn to have taken part in this uproar, was there laid a fine of three shillings. Out of this there was paid to the Proctor six marks for the solacing of his hurt and for the payment of the physician that did wait upon him. And as for the student that by his frolic did first give occasion for strife, he was banished from the University for the space of one whole year. As for John Eliot, he escaped without fine or censure, for all that he was known to many on either side.

We two had other sport also, and of a more laudable kind. Thus John Eliot would take his cross-bow—for which weapon both he and I had no small liking, as being that which at the first had brought us together—and shoot hares and rabbits in Bagley Wood and the fields thereabouts, having first obtained the grace of Master John Dennis, to whom the said wood and its appurtenances belonged. And I would go with him, but the cross-bow I never handled, being better content to see him handle it, which indeed he slid with a skill that was beyond compare. So sure of aim was he, that the keeper of the deer in the park would make request to him that he would kill such as were needed for the table, a thing which may not be done at hazard or by an unskilful hand. Verily the keeper who should lodge a bolt in the haunch of a stag, as is not unlike to happen when it flieth before him, would of a surety lose his place.

Then again I would take my angle, sometimes to Cherwell and sometimes to Thames, for in both of these rivers there is a notable store of fish, if you are content to go somewhat far afield, as to Sandford and Bablock and Islip. And in the matter of angling I did get much instruction from one Master Hevor, Prior of the scholars of the Black Friars at Gloucester Hall. Master Hevor was a monk of St. Albans, and had charge of such scholars as purposed to take the vows in the said Abbey (of which matter I shall say more hereafter). He did lend to me for my reading a certain little book which was written by Dame Juliana Berners, Prioress of the Convent of Sopwell, on this same topic of angling; from which said book I learned many things, especially about the taking of pikes and roaches. And as I would stand by and mark John when he did shoot, so would John stand by when I handled the angle, for which pastime he had small liking, affirming that it needed more patience than he could command. "Of watching the line," he would say, "I weary right soon; but of talking to thee, friend Thomas, I weary not." And I do verily believe that he loved me even as I have ever loved him.

In the year 1459, being the fourth year of my sojourning at Oxford, we two purposed to answer of our degree of Bachelor. And this we did, beginning on the eighth day after Ash-Wednesday, and continuing to answer for nine days (nor was this time beyond that which is customary, and indeed I have heard that the questioning hath been continued even until the end of the term). There are two-and-thirty masters that sit in the schools; and all these have the right to lose, for so the putting of questions is called, but some are content not to exercise it. Also they may put what questions they will, only the Chancellor, or his deputy, or the Proctors, may intervene, if it should seem to them that such questions go beyond fairness and reason. And of this I had myself experience, to my no small thankfulness. For one Master Lawrence, posing in a book of Aristotle, being one that loved the reputation of asking such questions as none could answer, was like to have put me into a sore dilemma. Saith Master Lawrence, "Doth not St. Paul the Apostle commend the virtue of humility as being singularly fitting to a Christian man, and that more than once?" "Yea," answered I, "he doth." "And doth not Aristotle, when he placeth virtue in the mean between two extremes, name *humilitas* or humility as an extreme which erreth by defect, even as arrogance erreth by excess, greatness of mind being in the mean? How dost thou reconcile these two? Dost thou hold with Aristotle, or with Paul?" And when I knew not what to answer, saith one of the Proctors, "Nay, Master Lawrence, thou dealest with this lad as thou wert a bishop, holding inquisition of a Lollard or other heretic. Why lost thou shut him up to a choice which he may not conveniently make either this way or that?" So did I joyfully escape from the jaws of Master Lawrence.

Verily I would not praise myself; yet may I say that I answered not without applause, as also did John Eliot, for we were in close company during this whole time. Especially well did we acquit ourselves in the School of Rhetoric, where one Master Butler, a master of Exeter College, did question us about the eighth and ninth book of the *Ethica* of Aristotle, wherein friendship is treated of. For these books, it so chanced, we had read together with notable care. And when Master Butler asked us of Cicero's treatise on Friendship, commonly called the *Laelius*, here also he found us well prepared. And when desirous to know whether we knew more of Cicero, it so chanced that he lighted upon his book "Concerning the Orator," which book also we had but lately read. Thus did we gain reputation beyond our deserts, being favoured by Fortune, who though she never helpeth them that are altogether without deserving, doth undoubtedly impart of her favour more liberally to some than to others.

The posing ended, we were admitted to the degree of Bachelor. And after, we that were so admitted gave to the Masters gowns and hoods, or a composition in money to such as chose money; also we gave a feast plentifully furnished both with flesh and fish, though indeed it was the season of Lent, for we had a dispensation.

OF JOHN ELIOT'S HOME

AFTER the Commemoration of Founders and Benefactors in this same year, the vacation being now nigh at hand, saith John Eliot, "Thinkest thou not, Thomas, that we two have applied ourselves to our books as never yet did two since this University was set up—or, shall I rather say, since books were first writ? What sayest thou to a holiday?" "Yea, with my whole heart," said I. Then saith he, "And where shall we better spend it than at my father's house? He hath had somewhat to say to thee these three years and more, and blameth me in every epistle that I do not bring thee. I too would fain see him, for he groweth old, and hath been somewhat shaken of late with sickness. There is my mother also, and the maids my sisters, and young Will my brother, who must be grown a proper lad. It is nigh upon six years since I saw them. Canst thou be content to bestow thyself for a matter of two months or thereabouts in a yeoman's household? Thou shalt be welcome for my sake at thy first coming, and after, I know it well, for thine own. Of sport thou shalt have that which thou lovest best, angling to thy heart's desire, for Severn limiteth my father's farms on the one side, a stream which may compare with Thames himself. In him thou shalt take the very king of fishes, even the salmon, who seemeth to me not to love

Thames overmuch, so seldom doth he come, but is as frequent in Severn as are the chevenders in Cherwell, where he floweth under the shadow of trees. And if thou canst not be content to live so long without books, we have more than be often found, yea, even in a knight's household. For my mother was sister's child to Sir Richard Warrington, a very learned clerk, that was Parson of Wednesbury in Shropshire, and had the inheritance of his books. And as for travelling, there has come in our way such a chance as could not have been looked for. Yestereven I found at the door of the Angel hostelry a certain priest from Shropshire that is of my kindred. When we had greeted one another, saith he, 'Well met, Cousin John. I was even now about to seek thee at thy college, having a certain matter wherein thou canst serve me. I am lately promoted by favour of the Lord Chancellor to a benefice in London, and am even now on my way to take possession. And I have with me Thomas Ball, that hath been my servant for these twenty years past, as perchance thou knowest. The simple fellow would not leave me, but must with me to London, though what he will do in the city God knoweth. But Thomas was ever master in such things, and I was content to obey. So we two have ridden hither from Shrewsbury, and, if I could sell our horses to no great damage, so I would do, and finish our journey in the waggon. Knowest thou then any honest man in Oxford with whom I may safely have dealings in this matter?' 'Thou askest a hard thing, Cousin Edward,' I made answer, 'for honesty and the buying and selling of horses are not close friends. Yet doubtless I can help thee.' Then, as I pondered the matter by myself, there came into my head, in one flash as it were, this counsel: We two will buy my cousin's horses, and will ride them slowly and carefully to Shrewsbury, so that they shall be in good case when we are arrived thither. And I will sell them at Shrewsbury fair, not, I warrant thee, without profit. So shall we have somewhat of advantage, and my cousin no damage. But, say, wilt thou come? for verily if thy good will be wanting, my whole counsel is naught." "Yea," said I, "I will come. And thy counsel concerning the horses is notably wise. Say, shall we leave being scholars, and become chapmen in horses? Thou shalt be the master, and I the man." That will we conclude," saith he, "when we have counted the profit on our first venture. But now let us away to my cousin the priest." And when we were come to the Angel we found him in the stable, looking with a countenance somewhat rueful at his horses. And when he turned and saw us, he said to John Eliot—for I lagged somewhat behind as being a stranger—"And is this thy honest dealer, Cousin John? Verily I thought not to see him a boy, though he is indeed *puer ingenui vultus.*" And this the good priest said, not thinking that I could hear him. Then saith John, "Come forward, Master Dealer, and see whether thou canst come to an agreement with Sir Edward Ridley, Parson of St. Nicholas Cole Abbey in the city of London." So I came forward, and made obeisance, after the fashion which the townsfolk use when they have affairs with a person of dignity. Saith he, "Master Dealer, what wilt thou pay me for these two horses?" I made answer, "Name thy price, Sir Edward, for that is our manner of dealing in this city." Then he saith, "What sayest thou to three marks for the two?" And I looked to John, and saw that he nodded to me as though he would say "yea." But that I might play my part the better, I made pretence to feel the beasts' legs, as one that tried whether they had any blemish or weakness; also I looked in their mouths, as one that would tell their age from their teeth, and not doing it, as I take it, after the common manner of dealers, was well-nigh bitten for my pains. And when I had made pretence enough, as I thought, I said, Thou shalt have thy three marks, Sir Edward," and straightway brought them forth out of my pouch. Then said the priest, "Verily this is the paradise of them that would sell horses, where there is no chaffering, or beating down of price, or talk of warranty; but the buyer taketh the seller's price, and asketh no question, and payeth down the money out of hand. I pray that the saints may prosper thee in thy dealings; but yet beware, for it is not every day that thou shalt meet with an honest priest—if indeed I may say so much on my own behalf." And John, when he heard this, laughed aloud, as also did I; and he said, "Cousin Edward, this is no dealer in horses, but Thomas Aylmer, Bachelor of Arts, and Demy of Magdalen College in this University." And thereafter he unfolded to him the whole plan. Then nothing would content the good priest but he must give back half a mark out of the three, saying, "This will make thy bargain the better, Master Dealer." And, that I may finish this portion of my tale, I will here say, that we sold the two horses for four marks at Shrewsbury fair.

After three days we set forth, for we would give the horses sufficient rest. Of our journey there is no need that I should write at length; happy is the traveller that path no adventure, and such happiness was ours. I did note that once or twice certain ill-looking fellows did eye us, as though counting up what we should be worth as a prey. But they seemed to judge, that, as we had the garb of scholars, our pouches were not like to be heavy; nor did they desire, for so small a chance of booty, to make acquaintance with John Eliot's staff. I do remember how noble a prospect there is from a certain hill which standeth between Oxford and Worcester, being named Broadway Hill; nor do I forget how first I saw Severn in this said city of Worcester, a very fair stream and spanned with a right noble bridge.

In ten days we came to Shrewsbury, from which town it is but an hour's easy riding to Master Eliot's house. Thither we came at seven of the clock in the evening—for I am not like to forget the very hour—and found Master Eliot and all his household gathered together, for it so chanced that he had that very hour ended the ingathering of the hay. They stood in the porch, looking at the men as they added the last waggon-load to the rick; and verily they were a comely family.

Master Eliot had some fifty-and-five years, but looked to be older. His shoulders were bowed somewhat, so that his stature seemed less than the stature of his son, though in his youth it had been equal at the least. Also his hair was gray, and his eyes somewhat dim and as though they regarded things far away (for so I thought when I first saw him and also afterwards). I judged so soon as I cast my eyes upon him that he had had great trouble in his youth, nor did I err therein. As for Mistress Eliot, one had thought that trouble had never come nigh to vex her, so blithe was she of look. At the first sight I judged that she must be Master Eliot's daughter, for there was never a gray hair in her head, nor a line upon her face. Mistress Joan had the same age as John, being his twin sister; and next to her was Mistress Alice, that had seventeen years or thereabouts; and after her again the youngest, Willie, a stout lad of fifteen, blue-eyed and yellow-haired, that had already five feet and nine inches of height, and promised even to surpass his brother. Mistress Alice was the very image of her mother, and might well have been counted her sister, save that she was somewhat slighter of shape, and her hair, when you looked upon it more closely, brighter of hue, and her eyes of a more lively sparkle. As for Mistress Joan—but how shall I write of her? Verily I could give her portraiture as I sit writing in this book, yea, and have given it not once only. God forgive me if I have done amiss! But if any one would see her similitude, let him look at the Rachel, daughter of Laban, whom I did paint for the great volume of the Vulgate that is now used in the Church, or the Virgin's which is in the Abbot's new *exemplar* of the Gospels. She was somewhat above the common stature of women, yet not over-tall, and straight as a palm-tree. Her face was of an oval form; her forehead somewhat high and broad for them that with the poet Horatius love the *tennis frons,* but noble of aspect. Her complexion somewhat brown, but clear and fresh, and with, as it were, a ruddy glow beneath. Her eyes a fair brown of such a colour as you shall not often see; and soft and tender beyond all telling. Her hair was somewhat lighter than one would look for in a woman so complexioned, for there were threads as of gold that sparkled in it. She smiled not rarely, yet not on every occasion, and laughed, I think, almost never. Indeed, there was a certain sadness in her look; so indeed I thought at the first seeing of her, and as I afterwards knew, not wrongly. But I saw it not save at the first, not only because of the sweetness and graciousness of aspect and manner, with which—for I may write the truth at once—I was wholly overcome, but because she was ever careful to keep her troubles from others, and to make others sharers of her gladness only.

The house was somewhat above a yeoman's station. In truth it had been a manor in time past, and had yet somewhat of the look and furniture of such. Chiefly it had a hall, both high and spacious, on whose walls hung three or four helmets, and coats of mail, and swords and lances. One of the coats of mail, I noted, was of chain armour, such as hath not been worn in this realm for two hundred years. Also over the fireplace, which, for greatness, might have served our hall in college, hung two long-bows. There was in this a shovelboard, of which more hereafter; and chairs of oak with velvet of Genoa, finely embroidered. We sat not in the hall, but, for the most part, in the kitchen, which, sooth to say, was of a more cheerful aspect, looking out upon the garden. Than this garden never have I seen a fairer and more fruitful spot. It had great plots of strawberries, which indeed were well-nigh past at our coming, yet lived again in Mistress Eliot's conserves; and cherries, white and red; and plums, of which, both of the red sort and the yellow, we had, for the greater part of August and September, such abundance as can scarce be conceived. Here, too, there were of every hind, borage, and lavender, and peppermint, and sage, and flowers as many as might have satisfied Queen Flora herself—roses red and white, which here grew together in peace, and pinks, and snapdragons, and sweet-williams, and a hundred others which it were long to enumerate. It was a very Eden in my eyes.

And that very evening I had proof, if indeed I needed it, that John had not deceived me concerning the salmon. For as I stood by that side of the garden which overlooketh Severn, running some hundred yards away, I noted a place where there was a fall in the water. And as I looked, behold a great fish, whose sides sparkled even as silver in the sun (which was now low in the heavens), leapt as though he would come at the water that was above the fall; and I saw that he had, as it were, bent himself into a bow, putting his head and his tail together, for his leap. And when he had fallen back into the water, for he failed of his purpose, there leapt another, and after him another, and so many more, of whom the greater part, it seemed to me, failed, but some got their end. And so it went on for the space of about one quarter of an hour; and then the fishes suddenly ceased to leap even as they had begun. While I looked, cometh John and clappeth me on the shoulder, with, "There is sport for thine angle, Thomas, to which Thames cannot compare."

After this we supped, I sitting by Mistress Eliot, with Mistress Joan on my right hand. I, that had never spoken with a woman for eight years and more, save once at Ascensiontide, when I sojourned for a sennight at home, was at the first not a little confused, but after got courage, so gracious was the maiden yet modest withal. And after supper we sat awhile in the garden, for the night was still and warm, and John led me to speak of many things, both grave and gay, till I was well-nigh ashamed to think how much I had discoursed. And she—for already my thoughts were of her only—listened, as they say, with both her ears. And when we went within, she laid her hand on my hand, lightly and but for a moment, as though she were half afraid, saying, "I know what thou hast done for my brother, who is as my life to me—for is he not twin-born?—and keep it in my heart." And her voice brake as with tears, which indeed I, at that instant looking up, saw in her eyes. Her father also, as I turned to my chamber (and they had bestowed me in the very best that there was in the house), said, "Think not that I forget if I am scant of words. Verily thou shalt be as another son to me, if thou wilt."

Then I climbed to my chamber, wherein was braver furniture than I had ever before seen: a bedstead notably carved with flowers and fruit, and a coffer of oak for my clothing, which did but scantily fill it, and chairs of like pattern with them that were in the hall. But nothing did I see more gladly than some roses, white and red, in a pot of blue ware, for I made bold to guess by whose hand they were plucked. And when I slept I had many dreams, of which some were glad and some troubled. But which of these came from the ivory gate, and which from the gate of horn (Virgil hath it that true dreams come from the gate of horn and false from that which is of ivory), I knew not, as indeed it is not in mortals to know, for indeed God doth wisely hide from us the issues of that which is to be, and revealeth them not, save but on rare occasions by vision or dream.

OF MY LIFE IN SHROPSHIRE

SOMETIMES I doubt whether I do well to call to mind the days of my sojourn in the household of John Eliot the elder, being, as I am, bound by vows to the religious life. Nor, indeed, do I deny that I was for the most part taken up with the love of Mistress Joan—a love which did begin with the very first sight of her; and that this love is a thing against which my heart is of necessity shut for ever. But verily—for I speak the truth and lie not—since the day when I did learn, as shall be told hereafter, that I had hoped in vain, there hath been with me no need of vows so to shut my heart. I should be single by choice if I were not single by profession. Yet I do not scoff and rail at the wedded estate, as do some of the brethren in this house, but count it, as indeed cloth St. Paul in his Epistle to Timotheus, a most honourable thing. And I do hold, that they who do live honestly and godly therein are not the less servants of God and men of religion than we who do specially take unto ourselves these titles. Nor do I count it shame that I did myself once aspire to this estate. For which reason, and because I find not that the remembering of these things maketh me unstable in the way that I have chosen, but rather refresheth and strengtheneth me, I have determined to write down in this book the sum of them.

The summer season of this said year 1459 was passing fine—unless, indeed, I do deceive myself, and do count the sunshine that was, if I may so say, in my heart, for that which cometh down from the heavens upon the earth. But doubtless it was without rain beyond what is to be commonly observed in this realm of England. I do remember especially that about harvest time there were many days in which, from the rising to the setting of the sun, there was not so much as the shadow of a cloud; and also, that Master Eliot did say there had never been a more prosperous and speedy ingathering of the fruits of the earth since he first had followed the farmer's life. In this ingathering we did all bear our part. Master Eliot himself did take the sickle in hand, though his wife and children suffered him not to labour during the heat of the day. As for John, for all that he had for many years handled book and pen only, his right hand had not forgot his cunning; and the lad William did service in the field beyond his years. There were three villains also that did labour continually on the farm; and to these there came out from Shrewsbury town three others who followed some handicraft at other times, but were wont to labour for hire at the ingathering of the hay and of the corn. As for me, I did essay at the first to handle the sickle with the rest; but when I had well-nigh done myself a damage, saith Master Eliot, "Nay, Thomas "—for the good man spake to me ever as to a son—"reaping is a handicraft, and may not be learnt by good will alone. At the best thou canst ply this tool but slowly, having given thy life to better things; and if perchance it wound thee, thou wilt hinder us sorely, taking the women from their work to cure thy hurt." After this I was content to help in such things as I was able to do, not being ashamed to bind the sheaves with the women; yea, being happy beyond measure in so doing when Mistress Joan was in the field. This was, for the most part, in the afternoon, for in the forenoon she was busy in the dairy with the making of butter, which at that season of the year is most conveniently done day by day. From the time when the sickle was first put into the corn until the stacks were fully made (but the thatching of the same was done after), was seventeen days, and there was never a drop of rain upon the corn from the beginning to the end. And when the harvest was ended, being the ninth clay of August, Master Eliot furnished a feast of ingathering, to which sat down he and his household, in the which I number myself, and the three villains and their wives, and the four men from Shrewsbury town with their wives also, but one was unmarried—fourteen in all; and there was much mirth and jollity, but nothing of riot and excess. And the next Sunday there was a thanksgiving in the church, which was finely decked with corn and flowers and fruits; and Brother John, a friar of the Order of St. Dominic, preached us a sermon, taking for his text, "Valles abundabunt frumento," for the parson of the parish, though he is an honest man and of a blameless life, is no preacher.

After the harvest there was a certain slackening of labour, though indeed the work of a farm never standeth still. Sometimes we would go down to Severn, where I would angle, the maids looking on and much applauding my skill. There on the twelfth day of August—for I do remember the day, nay, the very hour, for it was nine of the clock in the forenoon—I did first catch a salmon. How he did strive to quit himself of the hook, leaping in the air, and running with the river, so that I was fain to follow him with all the speed I might. For well-nigh an hour did I fight with him, thinking oft that I had lost him. And when at the last I brought him near to the land where the water was somewhat shallow, nothing would content Willie but he must leap in and thrust his fingers into the beast's gills, and so carry him to shore. And indeed I know not how without such help I should have handled him. He had a score of pounds in weight, wanting three or four ounces only. And though I caught not a few of his fellows after, there was not one of them so large.

In September we would sometimes go by night into the cornfields with a great net wherewith to catch partridges, taking of these, I do remember, some eight or ten at one time, and among them a quail or a landrail; also we did set snares in the hedges for hares, setting by the empty spaces where they were wont to run, and traps for the rabbits. Of these creatures there was no small abundance, and they do no little damage, especially in the spring season, devouring the corn while it is yet in the blade.

But the most notable day of the whole summer was the fifteenth day of September, when John did shoot a stag with his crossbow. The said stag had escaped in the spring season from my lord Shrewsbury's park at Ingestre, and had done much damage to the farms thereabouts, nor had my lord's keepers been able to kill him. Wherefore it was notified to the countryside, that they had license to shoot him if so be that they could. And this many had sought to do, and indeed had not lacked opportunity; but to shoot at so great a quarry doth, they say, unsettle the aim even of them that are well used to this sport. Certain it is that not a few had shot at the beast and failed. And now came tidings to John that the said stag had been seen by the river-side, where the grass was yet plentiful—for in the country round about it was scarce by reason of the drought. Then said I, "Wilt thou watch all night for him?" "Nay," said he, "that would but ill fit me for my work in the morning. But we will rise betimes in the morning, two hours at least before sunrising, and take our place in a certain copse that I know, and there wait till he shall begin his feeding, which he will do, I doubt not, with the very first dawn." And this we did. We rose about four of the clock, and about five had sight of the stag. Now there was much mist by the river, and the beast seemed, as the mist is wont to magnify, to be a very monster for size. And I whispered, "See the stag, John! Wilt thou not shoot?" "Nay," said he, "for he is nigh a furlong distant, and if I miss this chance I trow that I shall have never another. But we will get somewhat nearer to him. Wilt thou come, or wilt thou abide in this place?" "I will come with thee, and be Iphitus to thy Hercules," "Then follow me, and speak not another word, for if the beast see thee, or hear thee, or so much as smell thee (but happily the wind setteth from him to us), then is our labour lost." Then he stripped himself of his doublet and I also. This done, he crept on his belly along a ditch which had been dug by the side of Severn. It was for the most part dry; but in one place and another there was mud, and for the space of four or five yards at the latter end, water somewhat foul and ill-smelling, having half a foot in depth. This being passed, we came to another copse, of which when we had passed to the further side, lo! the stag was yet feeding, being distant about seventy yards, but stood with his haunches towards us. And I, raising myself from the ground, chanced to break the branch, which was of dead wood, whereon I laid hold; and the beast turning at the sound, John shot him through the heart. For he leapt once into the air, but after never stirred more. A goodly quarry it was, having forty stones of weight; and his horns, which my lord had reserved for himself, had fourteen points.

Sometimes, especially if the rain kept us within doors—though this, as I have said, did but seldom happen—we would play at chess or draughts, and sometimes also at shovel-board in the hall. For this last game there is a long table of oak, polished as smooth as may be, and at the end of the table and at the side thereof, for the space of four feet or thereabouts, a netting. 'Tis played with weights of brass, of three ounces or thereabouts, which the players push down the whole length of the table, striving who should place them nearest to the end. He doeth best that can leave them so as to abide hanging, as it were, over the end, for if they fall into the netting, then they are counted dead. And the players strive not only to bring their own weights to the best places, but also to drive therefrom the weights of their adversaries. For the most part Mistress Alice and I would contend against John and the lad Willie. As for Mistress Joan she would play but rarely, and when she played would not be content but that she must have sides with John, not bearing even in sport to be against him.

HOW I SAW THE BATTLE OF BLORE HEATH

AND now I must speak awhile of more serious things. When September was one-third spent, saith John to me, "Wouldst thou see something more of this fair county of Salop? If it please thee we will ride to Ellesmere, which is in the northern part, not far from Cheshire. There are goodly pools, which they call meres in those parts, full of such fish as thou shalt not often see. Put up thy angle, therefore, and we will ride and tarry there a week or thereabouts, and so back." And I, though I would have chosen rather a hundred times to abide where I could see Mistress Joan, could not, if it was but for friendship's sake, say nay; and so, feigning a contentment which was not in my heart, agreed to his counsel.

On the morrow, therefore, being the eleventh day of September, we set forth, and the next day came to

Ellesmere, nor had any adventure on the road; only we heard rumours of wars, for the peace which my lord Archbishop of Canterbury had made was altogether broken, and the armies of York and Lancaster were making themselves ready for the battle. At Ellesmere we were entertained by Master Tomkins, a maltster, and kinsman to Mistress Eliot. Sufficient of sport we had, I with my angle and John with his crossbow, shooting wild geese and the like, of which there was great plenty in those parts. Yet we were not altogether at ease, for the whole land was disturbed as if trouble were nigh at hand. On the twenty-second day of this said month of September we journeyed to Drayton, which is also called Market Drayton, for John had another kinsman there whom he would fain see. On the morrow, when we were now on the point to set forth journeying homeward, we were aware of a great stir in the town. And when we inquired the cause, we were told that an hour since (for it was then eight of the clock) there had come a rider into the town from my lord of Salisbury with a writing to the bailiff of the said town, that there should be made ready forthwith such provision of food and drink as might be got together. And the rider said that my lord had nigh upon ten thousand men with him, and that he was on his way to join himself with the Duke of York. Now when all had been gathered together, twenty carts full, so that there was scarce left in the whole town a loaf, or a cheese, or a quart measure of ale, the bailiff was in no small perplexity who should take charge of the provender to carry it to the army. "For," said he, "we would willingly take no side in these wars. Thanks be to God, Drayton hath no walls, for walls, though they do furnish defence against chance plunderers, are oftentimes a sore trouble to them that dwell therein. Wherefore it is the easier for us to live peaceably with all men. Nevertheless, if one of our chief men among our townsfolk should take charge of these goods he would be held to favour the one side. And yet to avoid waste and plundering there must needs go with them some one in authority." Thereupon said John, "Let me go, for I am a stranger in these parts, and yet not so much a stranger but that ye have warranty of my good faith. And within the space of a few days I shall depart to Oxford, where there shall be no inquiry what part I have taken in these matters." To this answered the bailiff, "So be it." Then said John to me, "Let us come; haply we shall see a battle, and though I would not for vain curiosity thrust myself into any place to which I am not called, yet if such a sight should fall to us while we do our duty, it were well worth the seeing." So we set forth, the carts following. And when we had gone a mile or thereabouts, we saw a company of horsemen. Then the rider of my lord Salisbury, setting spurs to his horse, hastened to meet them. And one of them rode back to the main army, which we now espied marching on the high-road, and in the meadows which lie upon either side of it. And in the front was a man of noble presence, and about him a company of thirty knights, or may be forty. Then said a certain trooper, "That is my lord of Salisbury, and the young men who ride on either hand of him are his two sons." And while we looked came one in the garb of a countryman riding at full speed, and a trooper with him. What the man said we heard not, being at two furlongs' distance; but we saw that he pointed northward with his hand. And looking thither we were aware of another army that marched from the westward, as though it would cut us off in our way. Now there lay before us a hill, with a fair plain of a mile or more every way on the top thereof, which they call Blore Heath, and it was between the two armies, but nigher to us, may be, by a furlong's distance. Then my lord of Salisbury bade sound on the trumpets that his men should quicken their pace, which they did so that they first gained the hill, and held already the greater part of the plain before their adversaries could come at it. Therefore I was the more astonished that the battle being but just begun, my lord Salisbury's men began to give ground, losing, for so it seemed to me, the vantage which they had. And I said, "They flee already, and are like to lose the day." "Nay," said he, "hast thou not heard of feigned flights? These men give ground in orderly fashion, and not as though they were possessed with fear. The end is not yet." Now there is a stream that divideth the Heath, shallow for the most part, but with deep pools. And I saw that the adversaries as they crossed the said stream brake their line, crowding together to the shallower parts. And before they could set it again in order my lord's archers, that were lying behind a certain rise that there is, let fly upon them a very storm of arrows. And ere they had recovered themselves, came my lord himself with his horsemen, five hundred at the least, and charged upon them. Then was there a very fierce battle, for a man could not choose between the two armies for strength, or courage, or numbers. Many knights and men-at-arms did valiantly on either side, and the archers on either side shot fast and with good aim. Nevertheless there remained with my lord Salisbury this advantage, and with his adversary—who was, as I after heard, my lord Audley—this damage, that the line of battle of the one was whole, and of the other broken. And so indeed went at last the fortune of the day.

I noted this of the knights, that such as fell came by their end in this way. They were clad in armour of proof so cunningly wrought that spear or sword could scarce do any damage thereto. But I saw that some were unhorsed, or were borne down man and horse together by the charge of some rider that was heavier of weight, or drave against them with some advantage, or came to the ground by the stumbling or wounding of their horses. And being fallen they could not by any means rise again for the weight of their armour, that which had been before their safeguard turning now to their undoing. And the billmen or the archers, who carried swords besides their bow, slew them as they lay upon the ground, having often much ado to come at any mortal part, so cunningly joined together was their armour.

One knight I did specially note, whom the billmen did thus kill, and that in a very barbarous fashion; a very horrible sight, such as l pray I may never look upon more. Of ransoming there was, I take it, but little. For in civil wars men slay rather than hold to ransom, not only because they have more heat one against another, but because they are ashamed to hold in prison sometime friends, whom, nevertheless, they are not ashamed to slay. Many men perished on either side in this battle, two thousand four hundred in all, of whom the greater part belonged, I heard say, to Cheshire, which shire indeed specially suffered, being divided against itself.

The battle being ended, my lord Audley, with such as were left to him—for besides them that were slain many had fled to their homes—returned westward by the way by which he had come; and my lord Salisbury went on his way to Pontefract to the Duke of York; but his two sons, being sore wounded in the battle, journeyed northward into Cumberland, where they might be more conveniently healed of their hurts. The two armies carried their wounded with them, save a few that chanced to have kindred in Drayton town. Of the knights and squires that were slain well-nigh all were taken for burial to their own homes, being, as I have said, for the most part of this country. Some few that came from far were buried in Drayton Church; for the common sort the townsfolk made great trenches upon the Heath and bestowed their bodies therein, not without due offices from the parson of Drayton and of other churches which are thereabouts. For two days we busied ourselves in these matters, and afterwards set forth for home, to which we came in two days' time, with great joy of the whole household, for they had heard that a battle had been fought hard by Drayton, and feared lest we might have been entangled therein.

Now it was time that we should take thought of our going back to Oxford. Therefore we had speech of a gatherer of scholars that purposed to journey from

Shrewsbury. With him we made agreement for hire of horses and other things needful.

On the first day of October (on which day we were to set forth) cometh Master Eliot, as I stood in the hall ready for my journey, and saith, "Son Thomas, if I may so call thee," and as he spake I caught him by the hand, as though to show my willingness, "it is meet that thou shouldst know to what family thou hast joined thyself. I am not of this country, but of the English border, as, perchance, thou hast already gathered from my name. My father was slain at Halidon Hill, which battle was fought, as thou knowest, fifty and three years since, at which time I was but a child of two years. And when I was come to thirty years my mother died, having had much trouble, for the Border is an ill place for a woman that is a widow, nor would she take another husband. Then I, being left alone, without brother or sister, and having small regard for my kinsmen and namefolk, who for the most part did live by robbery, caring nothing so that they did their plundering on the other side of the Border, I sold my holding to my lord Percy and came southward, having some hundred gold pieces in my pouch. And chancing on Drayton town, I fell into the company of a certain yeoman, Tompkins by name, an old man, having one daughter of his old age. Her I wedded, and lived in much content till the old man died. But when his kinsfolk were ill content that the land should pass to another name, we made agreement with them for a sum of money, and yielded the estate. Not many days after I bought this house wherein we stand of an old knight, Sir Louis Delisle. The said knight had wasted his means in his youth, living riotously with King Richard, second of the name, and his sons were dead, having been slain in France fighting against the Maid. So I bought the house and that which remained to it of the land, but the greater part had been sold beforehand, and also all the furnishing of beds, and tables and chairs, and other things which doubtless thou hast noted as being somewhat beyond my station. It was covenanted between us that the old man should dwell here to his death; and this he did. That chain armour that thou seest was worn by one Sir Thomas Delisle at the battle of Evesham, and that other by yet another Sir Thomas at Poictiers. But the bow that hangeth over the chimney was my grandsire's."

When he had ended came Willie, saying that the horses stood saddled at the gate. So after farewells given and taken we departed. But I noted that when I kissed Mistress Joan upon either cheek she neither trembled at all or changed colour; and with this, though I was not learned in the signs and tokens of love, I was ill content. As for me, of what aspect I was I know not; but my heart beat so fiercely that it seemed like to have broken from its place.

OF BISHOP WILLIAM AND OTHERS

I HAVE not many things to write touching my sojourn at Oxford before I did proceed to the degree of Master of Arts. But whereas before I had doubted what manner of life I should follow, inclining rather to the priesthood, as one in my place was like to do (for none may be fellows at Magdalen College but priests only), I was now steadfastly purposed to follow the law.

And this purpose I declared, as in duty bound, to the good Bishop when he came, as his custom was, to see his college on the Feast of St. Mary Magdalen, he himself giving me occasion of speaking. Saith he, "Nephew Thomas, what hast thou in thy mind to do? I have heard a good report of thee, how thou didst answer for the degree of Bachelor of Arts with much applause of all that were present, and hast always borne thyself soberly and discreetly; wouldst thou be fellow of this college, if I can so order it? only, as thou knowest, none are fellows here but such as are priests already, or, at the least, minded to be so in due course. And this I say to thee because I doubt nothing of thy honesty, but know that thou art not such one as would desire to be put into one of the priest's offices that he may eat a piece of bread. Hast thou then, thinkest thou, a desire or calling to the office of the ministry?" But when I knew not what to answer, but stood shamefaced, the Bishop looked at me more closely, as if he would read the secrets of my heart; and verily his regard, I had before noted, was exceeding keen. And after awhile, he steadfastly regarding me, and I, not so much as lifting my eyes from the ground, while my face burned, as it were, with fire, my good lord said, "Come now, Nephew Thomas, make confession; thy shame, I warrant, if indeed I have any skill in reading the countenance of man, is not other than honest. Thou art not—but who can answer for youth and love?—thou art not wedded already?" "Nay, my lord," I made answer;" I could not so forget my duty." And then I told him my story, not without beginning at the time when he had himself given the place of demy to John Eliot. And when I had made an end, he said, "And so thou wilt take Mistress Joan for such service as thou didst to Master John. I had not thought thee such an usurer. But, say, doth the maiden consent?" Then I said that I had not spoken, as not knowing what means of livelihood I might have; but that I hoped that she had, at the least, no misliking for me. Then the Bishop was silent for the space of three or four minutes; and after he said, "'They that marry,' saith the holy Apostle Paul, 'shall have trouble in the flesh;' yet have they also manifold blessings, of which not the least is this, that they are constrained to think of others rather than of themselves. As for thy livelihood, I will set thee in the way to earn it. Fellowship or benefice thou canst not have; but if, as I do conjecture, thou art purposed to follow thy father's calling, thou shalt not lack my good word. And when thou hast persuaded Mistress Joan, fail not to advertise me of your agreement, so that I may myself, if it be possible, join your hands, and find you somewhat for the plenishing of your house."

At these words of the Bishop I greatly rejoiced. But before many days my joy was dashed as I will now tell. I had, as I have before written, a sister that was a nun in the Priory of Godstow. It was my custom to see her once in the month, for more the Prioress suffered not, commanding that all scholars of Oxford desiring to see a kinswoman that was of the house should come on one day only. A fair building is this same Priory, hard by Thames; and the nuns have a church to which the country folk resort, very great and stately, that was built, as I have heard tell, by King Stephen; and also a chapel for their private use, near to which is the tomb of Rosamund de Clifford, who was surnamed the Fair. Her, for all that she had but an ill repute in her life, yet, because she was a benefactor to their house, the nuns suffered to be buried in their church, nigh to the high altar, and adorned her tomb with many adornments; and when St. Hugh, sometime Bishop of Lincoln, being visitor of the said Priory, commanded that the bones of the said Rosamund should be cast out of the church, they buried them hard by their own chapel. A very fair garden also they have, with a stream of clear water encompassing it, planted with all manner of sweet herbs and comely flowers.

When I came into the parlour I saw not there my sister, but the sub-Prioress only, who said, "Sister Agnes" (for that was Alice's name in religion) "is in great weakness of body, so that she had not strength to come into the parlour. And the cause is this. Thou knowest that we receive into our house certain young maids to teach and train. Of these one, newly coming from her home, though she seemed to be in good health, had yet a fever upon her. And this so spread, that in the space of ten days there lay sick eight in all, of whom some were like to die. Then Sister Agnes, to whom Our Lady hath given such gentle and gracious ways that sick folk do dearly love to be tended by her, did give herself over to the work of nursing these young maids, scarce departing from their chamber day and night, and then only by strict command of the Prioress. And now the maids are recovered (and Master William the leech saith that, after God, it is thy sister that hath worked their cure), but she is grievously sick, not indeed of the fever, for that she hath escaped, but of weariness: but come, for she looketh to see thee." So I followed the Prioress to a little chamber where they are wont to bestow such sick persons as are in most desperate case, as I was afterwards told. And when she saw me she beckoned with the hand that I should bend down my head, being scarce able to speak for weakness. So I kneeled down by her side, and she said: "Oh! Thomas, I had thought that God had set me in this place that I might pray for you that are without in the world. For you will have many cares and temptations; but here is peace and safety, so that I can care not for my own soul only, which surely it were a base thing to do, but also for them whom I love. But now I perceive that He hath ordered it otherwise. Wilt thou not then give thyself to His work, taking the vow in some house of religion, that when I shall have departed hence there may yet be some one to pray for them that are without." But I could not answer her a word, for it seemed that in a moment's space all my light was turned into darkness. And at the last I said, "O Alice, this is a hard thing thou askest. There is one—" but more I could not for the tears rose in my throat and choked me, and that not for myself only, but for her, to see her lying in such case. "Art thou promised, then?" said she, knowing not from my words only, but also from my face, what was in my heart. Then I answered, "Not so, yet I have a hope." Then I told her how the good Bishop had consented to the thing. And when she heard this she said, "If I had known this sooner I had not spoken. Nevertheless it was laid upon me to speak, or so, at the least, it seemed, for all now is darkened to me. But I ask no promise from thee; God will order these things as He will." Then I began to recover myself, and would have cheered her, saying, "Be of good courage; thou shalt pray for us all yet many years; and I will bring her for thy blessing, if all be well." "If God will," said she, "though indeed it is better to depart." Then she would hear what I could tell her of Joan Eliot; and as she lay listening with much content there came into her cheek, that was before deathly pale, the colour of the hedge-rose when the bud is now ready to break forth, and the dimness passed from her eyes, so that I began to have good hopes that she should do well. And when I parted from her, she said, "Thou wilt serve God, dear Thomas, whether thou be under rule or no." And these were her last words, for on the morrow she departed this life.

These things troubled me much; nevertheless I applied myself with all diligence to the study which I had chosen, hearing such as lectured on the canon law and the civil law, and not neglecting to be present in the schools if any disputed on such matters. And it was my purpose, when the proper time should have come, to enter myself at the Inner Temple, of which learned society my father had been a member until he was made serjeant. And when my mother heard of my intent, she sent to me certain books of my late father's, among which were many notes, written with his own hand, of cases wherein he had himself taken part, or at the hearing of which he had been present. Also there were judgments of notable judges and a book of the lectures of Master Thomas Littleton, who is, at this date of writing, one of the king's judges of the Common Pleas.

On the Feast of St. Mary Magdalen came Bishop William to his college. Dinner being ended he sent for me, and when he had inquired of my welfare, and how I prospered in my studies, he would know whether I had thoughts of any journey. Then I answered, not without blushing, that I purposed to set forth on the morrow for Shropshire. Thereupon he said, "Thou wilt return, as I suppose, to London, for thy work in this place is ended. Come therefore to me at my house in Southwark, and we will take counsel together what it were best for thee to do. And now I have a riddle which thou shalt guess, not now, but hereafter." And he took from his pouch a little coffer of cedar-wood, very fragrant, bound about with two cords of white silk, which were sealed with his smaller seal, that, to wit, which he was wont to use in his private affairs. This he gave into my hands, saying, "Here is a riddle, Nephew Thomas. Lo! I give thee this, and yet 'tis not for thee, but for another, and when thou shalt give it to this other, then shall it be thine." After this he gave me his blessing and let me go.

OF THE ELIOTS AGAIN

OF our journey into Shropshire it skilleth not to tell. Let it suffice to say that it was made safely and without mischance. The household at Berwick, for I have not as yet, methinks, told the name of Master Eliot's dwelling, seemed to me somewhat less cheerful than it had been at my first coming. Master Eliot himself was troubled of aspect and bare his years, which as yet were scarce threescore, more heavily than of old. These were, indeed, evil times for men that would live peaceably and mind their own business; and the dwellers in the country fared worse than the townsmen, for not only were they constrained to give up their hay and corn for scant payment, yea, oftentimes without price, great or small, but their fields were trodden down by the mere passing to and fro of armies. Also the whole country was overrun with sturdy vagabonds and masterful beggars, that had been wounded in the wars, or feigned themselves so to have been. Many knaves there be at all times who love to live idly rather than to work with their own hands; such did gladly take occasion by this war to follow their own ways, and did pretend themselves to be soldiers discharged for sickness or wounds, though they had never struck a blow either for York or Lancaster, or so much as seen a tented field. But there were also, in very truth, many who had been compelled by this war and by that which before was fought with such ill-fortune in France, to beg, as it were, upon the high-road. For some were maimed, having but one leg or one arm; and some were palsied (for sickness ever leaveth behind it more wounds than doth the sword), and many had lost such slender estate as they had. Verily, these were not days when a man could sit at peace under his own vine and his own fig-tree, but he must needs hold the plough or the sickle in one hand and the sword in the other, and be content with a portion, be it ever so small, of the fruit of his own labours.

Small marvel, then, if Master Eliot was like to one troubled with many things. Mistress Eliot, also, being, as a good wife should be, of one mind with her husband, was less blithe of aspect than before. Nevertheless, she bare bravely up, and failed not with comfort and counsel. As for Mistress Alice, that before was full of mirth and laughter, verily a "playful Galatea," as Virgil hath it of some nymph of the country, she was sobered, not altogether with care, but with happiness, being promised in marriage to a yeoman of fair estate that dwelt on the west side of Severn. This said yeoman, Robert Tudor by name, who had a far-away kinship with the Owen Tudor that did wed with Queen Katharine and was slain about this time at Mortimer's Cross, did come daily to Berwick; and Mistress Alice, though she had been wont to laugh at lovesick youths and maids, had no eyes for aught else when he was present, nor thoughts for aught else when he was absent. As for Willie, he had daily more and more the whole care of things upon his young shoulders, and was not a little burdened by it. Of Mistress Joan I have it not in my heart to write many words. Let it suffice to say that there grew up within me in those days a hope so strong that the breaking down thereof was like to have broken down my life. That she loved me I say not, and indeed know that it was not so. Yet did she begin to have for me such a regard as doth often, when it hath a prosperous course, lead unto love. And though at the first it troubled me, being, as I have before written, unskilled in such matters, that she seemed to behave less friendly, yet afterwards I noted, not without much pleasure, that she would turn her eyes to the ground when I spake, and would change her colour, nor would look me, as before, in the face. As for me, though I delayed, not being willing to risk so much without full assurance, to ask her love directly, yet I did sufficiently reveal that which was in my heart, being encouraged thereto by what Bishop William had said concerning my advancement in that course of life which I had chosen. And I do believe that there is never a woman in the world but is somewhat touched by the manifest love of a man, especially if she be of so tender a soul as was Joan Eliot.

This summer of the year 1462 was, I remember, as full of rain and storm as the same season nine years before, when I did first see Berwick, abounded in sunshine. The hay was yet in the fields when we came thither at the first beginning of August, and could not be gathered in till it had well-nigh lost all colour and savour; as for the corn, I saw some of it, in the low-lying lands, surrounded with water; nay, some was carried away by a great flood, which, as I shall hereafter write, did come down Severn from the Welsh mountains and carry him over all his bounds about the Feast of St. Michael. From these causes came no little care and trouble, and also much increase of labour, seeing that the work which was done on one day had to be done yet again on the morrow.

During these days it came into my mind to examine the books which, as I have before said, Mistress Eliot had inherited from a certain kinsman of hers that was a learned clerk at Wednesbury, in which books I found that which repaid my pains many times. This Sir Richard Warrington had travelled in Italy, a country which did then, even as it doth now, incomparably surpass this realm of England in the zealous following of learning. And in Italy he had fallen in with one Bracciolini, otherwise called Poggio, than whom there hath never been, from the days of the Romans themselves, any man more learned in the Latin tongue. With this man, of whose decease I do remember to have heard not long after my first going to Oxford, he consorted much at Florence, and was greatly furthered by him in his studies, as. I learned by certain notices which I found among his books. For this Poggio gave him free access to his library, in which there were to be found not only such books of the Latin writers as are commonly to be found in such places, but others also which were then newly discovered (in which business of discovery Poggio himself had had marvellous good fortune), and which even at this date of writing are known to but few only. Portions of these, but not the whole (either because of the too great cost or because the said Poggio would not suffer it), Master Warrington had caused to be transcribed for him. Among which writings was the first book of Lucretius, "Concerning the Universe," right noble poem, but of the detestable philosophy of them who say there is no God. But because I had turned my thoughts from arts to laws I did not give much heed to these matters, but rather to another volume which Master Warrington had brought with him from Florence, to wit, the *Digesta* of Justinianus, sometime Emperor of the East, wherein was included the whole body of the law of the Romans. And there was yet another book of which I must needs make some mention. It was a volume of some hundred pages, very neatly writ, and on the inner side of the cover, fastened thereto with paste, a letter which I will here transcribe, or rather translate, for it was of the most elegant latinity.

"Poggius to Richard Warrington, Greeting.

"I fear greatly that we shall never more interchange words with the living voice, for with both of us our age is far advanced, and there are between us, as Homerus hath it, 'the shadows of mountains and the roaring of the sea.' I send thee, therefore, as a pledge of regard and friendship, this book, which I have but lately purchased from a young Greek,

Constantine Dioscorides by name, that hath fled hither from the city of Constantinople, lately taken, as thou knowest, by the infidels. Many others of the same nation are there now in Italy, so that the Greek tongue, in which, as thou knowest, in time past few only bestowed so much as a thought, is now diligently learnt by many. Now I know thee to be one that will never cease from learning so long as life shall be left thee. Therefore I send thee these elements of the Greek tongue with the more confidence. For if Cato, being now an old man, learnt Greek that he might not be behind the younger generation, wilt not thou do the same that thou mayest read the words of Christ and His apostles even as they themselves spake them.

"Written this fourteenth day of March, 1454"

This book was a grammar of the Greek tongue, writ in Latin, having at the end thereof certain passages wherewith the learner might conveniently exercise himself, among which passages were certain portions of the Gospel of St. Matthew, and of the Acts of the Holy Apostles, and from profane authors certain fables of Æsop and verses of Solon, the same that did make laws for the city of Athens.

This book I showed to John Eliot, saying much of how precious it was. And in the space of two or three days after saith to me John Eliot the elder, his wife and children being present with him, "Thomas, though thou lookest, I know, for no rewards for thy service done to us, yet we would fain show by some visible proof and token that we are not ungrateful. Take, therefore, if thou wilt, this book, which my wife, we all consenting, giveth to thee." And he gave into my hands the book of the Greek elements, which I, though I was ashamed to take so precious a gift, was fain to receive; and indeed I keep it to this day, and shall keep it till I die.

OF EDWARD NORTON AND HIS STORY

THIS year was, as I have written, one of much rain and storm, so that we could not gather in the harvest but by little and little at a time, and that much damaged by long continuing in the fields. When this was at last done, Willie departeth on an errand for a certain town, whereof I cannot mind the name, but know that it was on the borders of Wales. And the errand was the selling of a horse, and the buying of another in his stead. This he did on the twenty-seventh day of September, and was to return on the second day, that is to say, the twenty-ninth day, being the Feast of St. Michael, which Master Eliot was always wont to keep as a holiday. Mistress Joan also was absent, sojourning with a neighbour whose daughter was sick, for she had a notable gift of nursing. Now in the afternoon of the day when we looked for Willie to return, Severn, who, I have noted, travelleth more quickly than Thames, as, having his birth not in the plain country but among mountains, began greatly to rise. And about six of the clock, when the sun had been now for some time set, and the light was beginning to be dim, cometh Willie to the ford that is above Master Norton's house five furlongs or thereabouts, and maketh essay to cross. We, that is, John Eliot and I, standing on the river's edge, warned him that there was danger, and bade him ride round by Shrewsbury bridge. "Aye," said he, for the night was still save for the rushing of the water, "and lose two good hours of time;" and so, without more ado, rode into the water. At the first he seemed to do well, keeping his horse's head very steadfastly against the stream; but, when he was two parts over, and was come to the strongest of the current, the horse, losing strength or courage (and it was newly bought and knew not the voice and hand of his rider), turned his head downward, and straightway was carried away, being whirled about as might a cork. Nor could we help, though John was a sturdy swimmer, for 'twas as much as a man might do to save himself in such a stream. But while we looked, with our hearts standing still as it were with fear, we were aware of a stranger that road down to the ford to the side whereon we were standing. The man we had scarce time to note, but his horse was such as I have never seen the like of it. 'Twas black of colour, and of such a stature and strength as could scarce be matched in Christendom. Not one moment did he tarry, but rode straight into the river, and coming to Willie's horse, which chanced by good fortune to touch for an instant on shallower ground, caught it by the bridle, and turned his head again up the stream. Then he spake to his own horse, whispering, as I could see, into his ear, and patting him on his neck, while with his other hand he held the bridle of the other (but the rein he held in his teeth). And so they came safe to the shore. And being landed, Willie fell from his horse, being utterly spent, and the horse also could scarce move from weariness. Then the stranger, who seemed to care for nothing, put a flask to the lad's mouth, and constrained him to swallow some cordial; and when he had somewhat revived, he put him on his own horse and walked by the side holding him. And we followed, but this very slowly, for Willie's horse, as I have said, was utterly spent, so that the stranger speedily outstripped us, and was lost to sight, we marvelling not a little that he should be so thoroughly acquaint with the way. And when we came to the house, Willie was in bed, with Alice his sister tending him, and the stranger stood by the fire in the kitchen alone, for both Master Eliot and his wife chanced to be abroad at a neighbour's house. When John cast eyes upon him—for before, as I have said, we had scarce noted him for the urgency of the business in hand—he was astonished like to one, if I may so say, that hath seen a spirit. And while he looked, seeming as if he could not so much as move his foot from the ground—but the stranger spake never a word, but only smiled a little—cometh in Master Eliot the elder. He, too, seemed for a while as though he had been stricken dumb. Then he ran and caught the stranger by the two hands, saying, "This is no spirit, as indeed I was ready to believe, save that spirits show not themselves in company, but flesh and blood. Ho! John, knowest not Edward Norton? But, say, Edward, whence comest thou? and where hast thou been these eight years? We thought thee dead. Verily this is a day of rejoicing, and all the more that thou art, I know well, no prodigal returned, but an honest man, as thou ever well." Then John ran to him and greeted him, as did also Mistress Eliot, chancing to come in at that same time. And I, seeing that this was a dear friend of old time come back, and minding that the wise man had said, "In gaudio ejus non miscebitur extraneus," I withdrew myself to my own chamber. But in a space of half an hour or thereabouts cometh John and biddeth me descend to supper. There was, I do now remember, something strange in his regard, as if he were scarce willing to look me in the face; but I understood not the thing, and it passed from me as such things are wont to do, and I descended suspecting nought. After supper, Willie also being present—for nothing would content him when he heard the news but he must rise from his bed, Edward Norton told us his story, which I will here shortly recount.

"Ye know how I took service with my lord of Shrewsbury, and passed with him into Gascony. There for a while he prospered exceedingly, though having but scarce three thousand men, and took many towns and fortresses. Bordeaux also he got, the townspeople sending to him that he should receive the city. So we came by night, or ever the Frenchmen were aware of the matter, and entered by the gate that had been left open for us. The Frenchmen perceiving this, fled by a postern, but were for the most part overtaken and slain. After this came my lord Shrewsbury's son with other nobles and knights, having with them two thousand men and over, and store of victuals and munitions of war. Then the Earl fortified Bordeaux, and, setting out thence, took many places thereabouts, the people for the most part desiring to return to the liberty they had under the English. But though we had prospered so far in our undertaking, it was an evil time such as, I do pray to

God, I may never see again. For the whole land was wasted with war. And much had been suffered to grow wild, as though it had never been inhabited. No man durst abide in the villages, for now the Frenchmen would come, and now the Englishmen. And if a man received the Frenchmen with friendship, then the Englishmen, returning, maybe the next day, would waste his goods as though he had betrayed them. And the Frenchmen would do the very same if he received the Englishmen, so that no man could be safe. And if he chanced to dwell so near to a stronghold of the one or of the other that he was not in peril of attack, then he found that his friends were scarcely less burdensome than his enemies. For the most part the peasants had fled into the towns, and made such shift as they could to cultivate the fields that were nigh to the walls. And when in the morning the men went forth to plough the ground, or drave out the cattle that they might have pasture, a watchman would climb up to the highest tower that there was upon the walls, and watch the country round about. And when he saw any company of horsemen approaching—and such were wont to ride daily about the land, seeking what they might devour—he would blow upon a horn that he had. Then the peasants left their work, and gathered up their tools, and hasted back to the town. And such as tended the cattle drave them back with all speed, though this they had scarce any need to do, for the cattle knew the sound of the horn, and hasted back of their own accord.

"Among other towns, the town and castle of Chatillon was delivered up to the Earl. This the French king besieged with a great army; and the Earl hearing thereof came with all speed to the rescue. And indeed the Frenchmen, hearing of his coming, left besieging the town, and retired to their camp, which they had trenched and ditched and fortified with ordnance. This camp the Earl assaulted, and had almost won the entry thereto when his horse was slain, and he himself shot through the thigh with a hand gun. Then was he slain, for the Frenchmen, who never durst look him in the face while he stood upon his feet, killed him lying upon the ground. With him also was slain his son, fighting his first battle. With many words did my lord entreat him that he would save himself, but he would not, preferring to die than to live on such terms. Many others was slain, and some threescore taken prisoners, of whom I was one.

"I fell into the hands of a very courteous knight, Sir Geoffrey de Brialmont. This knight, being commanded by the physicians to rest awhile, for he had been wounded, and the hurt, though it was but slight, did not heal, departed to his castle by the sea, and took me in his company. Then he kept me for two months in such sort that but for my desire for freedom, I had been well content. For I had entertainment of the best, and sport, hunting wild boars in the woods, and flying falcons for heron's paws, and plying tennis, a noble game of ball, which they do call the game of kings. And when September was nigh spent came news that Bordeaux was to be delivered up to the French on conditions that all the Englishmen that were in the Duchy of Aquitaine should depart, and that such as were prisoners should be set free. And now mark my ill fortune. The Knight and his people dwelt securely, having now no fear of the English, and left the castle, I take it, almost without watch. And the very night after the coming of these good tidings of liberty there came upon us an enemy of whom we had not so much as dreamed. A ship of rovers of Tunis, entering secretly in the darkness, anchored in the river that was hard by. About two hours before dawn cometh a company of these villains and assaulteth the castle—if I may call that an assault where there were none ready to resist. Some they slew, and some they carried off to their ship, and the castle they burned with fire. What I endured on the voyage—for the pirates, who were indeed loaded with spoils, sailed straight to Tunis—I cannot relate. We were ten prisoners in all, and lay in the hold all the night and day also, save for some two hours, when we were suffered to come upon the deck, five at one time and five at another. Of food we had but a scant supply; and of water, of which the villains were very short, but one pint by the day, and that of the muddiest. But when we came to Tunis there again fortune favoured me; for a division of the spoil being made, I was delivered to a citizen of the town who showed me such kindness as could not have been surpassed had he been a Christian man. May he have his reward, though he be an infidel! He put no chain upon me, as all other masters were wont to do, nor kept me in ward; but when I had given him my word that I would not escape, suffered me to go where I would (only for my safety's sake he permitted me not to go into the town). And he gave me for my work such light tasks as came to hand, and these chiefly in his garden, which was as fine an one as I have seen, with great orange trees, and lemons, and pomegranates, and palms, but wanting somewhat in the freshness of our English pleasaunces.

"With him I tarried for a year, and thence came by my deliverance in such a way as I could never have conceived. My master fell under displeasure of the Bey, for so they call the chief ruler of the city of Tunis, who seized all his goods, and among them his slaves, of whom I was one. Then I was marched to the Bey's palace and cast into a dungeon, not without complaints of my hard fortune in being separated from so kind a master, for how should I know that this evil would turn to my good? But so it was. But first I should say that there were others also who were in the like case with me. On the third day among the victuals that we had from abroad, by condescension of our jailer and by help of money, we found a melon. Breaking this open, for a knife we were not suffered to have, we saw therein a writing to this purpose, that if by any means we could escape we should find that night, and the two nights next following, at a certain place two miles westward of the harbour, those that would deliver us from our captivity; and there was with the writing a lump of clay, of which I could not at first conceive the use, till it appeared to me, by the inspiration I do verily believe of the saints, that it was for the making of a false key. Now I chanced to have upon me a knife in a pocket which the jailer, to whom our clothing was strange, had not searched. And first one of us that was a mechanic took with the clay an impression of the lock, and so we made a wooden key. Now we were fastened with a chain to an iron bar till our shackles should be made; and when night was come we sought to pick the lock of the chain with a prong of iron with which the knife was furnished. On this work we spent two hours, but it seemed to no purpose, till being wearied out we lay down to sleep. But about an hour past midnight there came into my heart the thought that I would try the lock yet once again. And this I did, and at the very first trial opened it. Then I woke my companions; and we opened the door of the dungeon with the wooden key. Then coming to another door we easily lifted it from the hooks with an iron bar which we there found; the same we did with a third with a door, which last led us into the street. This by great good fortune we found altogether empty, for it was the hour of the night when fewest are abroad. And the like fortune favoured us that we got clear of the town without meeting any man; and so, fetching a compass, came upon the sea-shore, where we found a boat waiting, with men from a ship of Venice. When we were come on board said the captain to us, 'I have good hopes of your deliverance; but I must use some policy. We of Venice are now at peace with these infidels. If, therefore, I should give them offence I should fall under the displeasure of the State, besides that the merchants on whose behalf I sail this ship have no small interests of commerce in this town. Were it not so, I would straightway hoist sail and depart. Now I doubt not that there will presently come certain to search the ship. Disguise yourselves, therefore; ye that have beards shave them off; ye that have none put on false with which I presently furnish you. And when the searchers shall come I will swear that ye are servants of the Republic; and ye must take like oath. And that we may do this with the better grace ye must sign this paper, wherein ye bind yourselves to serve the Republic for seven years. With this and two or three gold pieces to boot I doubt not that ye will escape.' And so indeed, by God's blessing, it came about."

After this Master Norton told us how he had served the State of Venice in many places, whose very names I cannot now remember. But the end of his speaking I do remember only too well.

"So when my term of service was ended, I embarked on a ship of Venice that was bound for Bristol. And from Bristol I journeyed to Whitchurch in this country, having an errand to the Earl of Shrewsbury from his late father. But him I found deceased, having been slain, as you know, in the battle of Northampton. But his son received me right courteously, and I delivered to him the message of his grandfather, with which he charged me when he lay dying at Chatillon. And my lord hath promised me a good place in his employ. Nor did I fail to gather in the service of these rich merchants of Venice a fair store of gold pieces, so that I came not back as penniless as I went forth. And every penny, as indeed hat been every thought of mine for these eight years past, is for my sweet Joan, if I may so call her with your good leave, Master Eliot."

When I heard this it all came upon me in an instant of time, that this was a lover of time past, and that indeed Joan had not been promised to him, lack of means forbidding, and her youth also, for she could have been but barely fifteen, and that he had been reported as dead, whence the sadness that I at the first noted in her, and that now he was come back. Then I rose from my place, and being favoured by the chance that Willie, not being wholly recovered, grew somewhat faint from long sitting and listening, departed without word said to my chamber.

I PROPOSE TO BECOME A MONK

ONE comfort I had in my great trouble, that I had not spoken of my love to Mistress Joan. That she had some knowledge thereof I did not doubt; for what woman is there that doth not discern somewhat, at the least, of the love that a man hath towards her. And mine of late I had not sought to hide, because I knew that her kinsfolk were well-inclined to me, and that a livelihood was assured to me by the good bishop, my patron, so only my own industry were not wanting; and because I hoped also that she herself was beginning to turn to me. And, indeed, I should have spoken, if the things of which I have just written had happened but only one day later. And that this was so was, as I have said, my one comfort. For if the maiden had given me her promise, as indeed she was not unlike to have done, being grateful for service done to her brother (to whom she was, as I have before written, singularly bound in affection), and knowing her parents' goodwill, and being persuaded in her mind (though indeed her heart still held out) that Edward Norton was long since dead, what trouble would there not have been. For she would have been divided between faith, of which she was ever most careful, and love; and Edward Norton, than whom there never lived in this world more loyal gentleman, would have been not less distracted between duty and honour, and I myself had been in the sorest strait that can be imagined. But now he knew nought of the matter; and she, though indeed she knew that I loved her, yet knew not how deep was this love; and as for me, I found the task set to me in this the easier, that what I had never possessed I was not constrained to give up to another.

This necessity indeed I felt to be laid upon me, that I must straightway depart. For Mistress Joan was to come back upon the morrow, and her I could not endure to see. Therefore I went about midnight, with my feet unshod, and stepping as lightly as I could, that none might hear, to the chamber of John Eliot the younger. And when I had knocked at his door, I found him watching, for he knew something, at the least, of my trouble. And when he saw me, for the lamp was burning on the table, he reached forth his hand, saying nothing. And I said, "John, I must away, so soon as ever it shall grow light. There is no need to speak the reason which indeed thou knowest; as I doubt not will thy father and mother also, and Alice also. But if Willie, who is but a boy, would know the cause of this sudden departure, thou wilt quiet him as best thou canst. What I shall do hereafter, at this instant I know not for certain, though I have certain thoughts in my heart. But first I go to Oxford, and when I shall have further determined, then I will advertise thee of my purpose." "But how wilt thou go," saith John. "On foot," I made answer; "and what things I have here thou wilt take such occasion to send as may come." Then John reached forth his hand again to mine, and so stood till he could find words to speak, for he was sore troubled in heart. At the last, he said, "Thomas, this is a matter in which it were better to say a few words than many, and best, it may be, to say nought. Comfort I cannot give thee; God shall give it thee in His time, for He doth not altogether desert them that love Him, as I know thou dost. But, say, thou dost not repent that we two have been friends, and that I brought thee to my home, and made thee known to my kinsfolk? I know in what trouble it hath ended; yet I cannot wish in my heart that it had been otherwise." "No," said I, "that will be a joy to me for ever. Whatever betide, I do thank God from my heart that I have found another father and mother, and brothers and sisters, in this household." And when I had thus said I left him.

The next morning at five of the clock, when it was now just beginning to grow light, I came down from the chamber. And lo! John had lighted a fire in the kitchen, and made a hot stoup of ale hot with spices and toasted bread, which I made shift to drink, not having much appetite thereto. Also he had prepared some provision of food by the way, as much as I could conveniently carry. And he gave me a stout oaken staff. Nor would anything serve his turn but he must go with me so far as Shrewsbury town. This he did, but though we walked together we scarce spake a word by the way, not for lack of goodwill, but because our hearts were overfull for words. And when we were gotten on the further side of Shrewsbury town—but the town itself we left on one side lest perchance some acquaintance should espy us—we kissed one the other, and parted with no more than "God speed," but I trow that our hearts had never been more drawn together than they were that day. I have not seen John Eliot since our parting; but I am persuaded in my heart that I shall see him before I die.

So I journeyed towards Oxford. And at the first I was so much taken up with my great sorrow that I could not so much as think what I should do; only my heart was utterly set against the way of life which I had before chosen. It may well be that some one reading this that I have written may charge me with weakness, saying, "Shall a man then mar his whole life because he is crossed in love?" Nor do I deny that such an one may be in the right. I set not up myself for an example, God knoweth. Nay more, I do readily confess that I lack the strength which doth win its way to an end, all hindrances notwithstanding. I have, if I may so say without vain glorying, certain gifts; for I love beautiful things, and have some skill in picturing them, and there is at times the grace in me to speak comfortable words to such as are in sickness or sorrow or any affliction; and patience also I have, for which indeed I do most heartily thank my God, that I may endure the burden which is laid upon me; but the strong heart and good courage that rise up against trouble and overcome, these I have not. And I do count it a singular proof of the wisdom with which God hath ordered the things of this world, that for such as I am there have been set up in Christendom such pious foundations as that wherein I have now found a safe refuge.

On the third day of my journeying I came to Worcester, where there is a fair Priory of the Benedictines; and being somewhat spent with my journey—for I had had small care of meat and drink, and it had been a time of much rain and cold—I asked at the gate whether I might have shelter for the night. Nor was I altogether sure in my mind that I should have a good welcome, for wandering scholars be not always guests to be desired. But when I declared my degree to the porter he received me with all courtesy, for which he had, as I heard afterwards, strict commandment from the Prior. Now it chanced to be a great day, and the Prior supped with the brethren in the refectory, and when he heard that a certain Master of Arts, and of Magdalen College withal—for this also I told on questions being asked—was come, nothing would content him but I must sit at his right hand, for he was a great lover of learning, and a favourer of all who do follow her though but in a humble degree. So I sat in high place, though indeed so worn was I and travel-stained, I would fain have sought a lower room. Then we had much talk together about books, and I—for I could not but put away for a while mine own troubles, so kind and courteous was he, for all that he was a great man—I spoke of all that I had of late read, and especially of the little book of the Greek rudiments of which I have before written.

It was a right noble feast; for the table was set with silver dishes very fairly made, and that which was set before the Prior was silver gilt. And to each guest there was a cup of silver; the meats were beef and mutton, and geese and capons and partridges. And there were set also great silver pitchers of wine, both of Burgundy and Bordeaux. But for all that there was such abundance, none, for so it seemed to me, did exceed in meat or drink; and as for the Abbot, so intent was he on his talk of learned matters that he cared not what he did eat or drink. And after supper the reader, standing in a pulpit that was by the Abbot's table, read in a very sweet and tuneful voice, the Life of St. Hugh, sometime Bishop of Lincoln, writ by Adam, that was his chaplain and after Prior of Eynsham. And when I marked what peace and plenteousness was within these walls, and how harmony and the fear of God with all temperance and sobriety, for so I deemed, did dwell there, it seemed that they who followed such a life had chosen well.

That night I was bestowed in one of the guests' chambers, and at the first, for the bed was soft and pleasant, and I was wearied with my travelling, I slept. But about half an hour before sunrise, when there was just so much of light that I could discern the casement, I awaked out of my sleep, or so I thought. But haply I was not indeed awake, but sleeping in such wise as I have sometimes noted in myself, wherein a man seeth all that is in his chamber and seemeth to be awake but is indeed asleep. But that which I saw was this—but whether it was a vision or a dream, as I knew not then, so now I pretend not to judge. There seemed to stand by the window my sister Alice, of whose decease I have before written, habited as a nun. Round about her head was a ring as of pale gold, it might be a hand's-breadth wide, and her countenance was as if there were a light beneath it, so did it shine and glisten. And as she looked upon me there was in her eyes even such a smile as that wherewith she had bidden me farewell, but brighter, for indeed God had wiped away from them all tears. She spake never a word, no nor yet beckoned with the hand; and yet it seemed that she drew me with such drawing as I must needs yield to. Nevertheless I could neither speak nor move. And in the space of two minutes, as near as I could judge, she vanished out of my sight.

After this I slept no more, but lay and mused on what I had seen or dreamed. And I did not doubt that it was a message to me that I should follow the religious life. And indeed that which before I had thought most hateful now seemed altogether to be desired.

The Prior would have me abide the next day and rest myself; which I was not loath to do, being weary and footsore. And I dined with him in his private chamber, the sub-Prior also and the Master of the *Scriptorium* bearing us company. And when these went their ways after dinner I was moved to open my whole heart to the old man, for he seemed as a father to me. And when he had heard both my life in the past and what I purposed in the future, he said, "I will not advise thee this way or that. Ponder the matter well with thyself, and be not hasty to do that which cannot be undone. I indeed am well content with my lot; but know that all is not peace within these walls, for all that they seem to be so peaceful. And there are houses which are houses of God in name only. *Corruptio optimi pessima,* which words I do not need either to translate to thee or to expound. Verily if a religious house, where learning and piety and brotherly love do abound, be as heaven, that wherein not these things, but ignorance and idleness and lust and hatred do abide is as hell. A thousandfold better wert thou in the world than in such. Take heed therefore of thy ways." Then he gave me his blessing and let me go.

I ENTER THE HOUSE OF ST. ALBANS

BEING come to Oxford—and this I did on the Thursday after my departing from Worcester—I judged it best that I should go without delay to the Prior of Gloucester Hall, which place the Order of St. Benedict set up for the training of such scholars as should become brethren in their houses. Of the Prior of the said hall I had had some knowledge, and going to him and declaring my purpose I was exceeding well received. For indeed I had some little repute in the University, being known to have disputed for my degrees not without success, and to have the favour of the Lord Bishop of Winchester. And indeed for some time past there had been a certain decay in the number of those who sought to be admitted into the brotherhood of the monasteries; and yet more in their condition and dignity. Some of the smaller houses that had but poor estates could scarce find enough for their necessary offices; and the greater, though indeed they had no lack of men seeking to be admitted, were content to take not a few of low degree and little learning. And this evil—for such it is—is like to increase, seeing that there are year by year new ways of life opening, so to speak, before the eyes of men. So it was that I was received with no small honour and welcome, though it was needful that I should wait for the coming of the Lord Abbot of St. Albans—for this house slid I purpose to enter—before I could be in due form admitted.

When this was accomplished it was needful that I should be instructed in such things as a monk should know. And first the Prior would have me taught the art of plain singing, which art I was willing to learn, though indeed I doubted much of my ability thereto, and this not without reason. For when the teacher of' plain song would try my voice and sounded a note whereto, for so he said, I was to answer, I, scarce knowing what he meant, but seeking to do my best, uttered so strange a sound that he and the Prior, and one or two others that were present, did incontinently stop their ears. Then said the teacher, "'Tis incredible that a Christian man should be so like unto an owl," for I have noted that they who have knowledge of any art do commonly fail to understand why others should perceive that which they themselves do see. "Nay," said the Prior, "Master Aylmer hath gifts though they are not of this kind;" and to me, "'Tis manifest that it were lost labour to teach thee singing. But there are other ways of serving God. Canst thou write a clear hand?" And he bade him sit down at the table and write. And when I had written two or three lines, he, looking over my shoulder, clapped his hands softly, and said to the teacher of song, "Master Sharpe, there be twenty that can sing for one that can write like this youth." To me he said, "My lord Abbot loveth a skilful clerk above all others, and he will be right glad to hear of thy coming."

Not many days after cometh to the hall the said Abbot, by name John Wheathampstead—or rather John Bostock, for Wheathampstead was the place of his birth—of whom it is meet that I should write somewhat, seeing that none greater, whether you regard his learning or his capacity, path sat in the principal place of this house.

The said John was prior of the scholars in Gloucester Hall, from which place he was promoted in the year 1420 to be Abbot of St. Albans, being then not more than seven-and-thirty years of age. Being so advanced, he found that by the neglect of them that had gone before, the buildings of the Abbey, and more especially the church, had fallen into great decay. And because the revenues of the house, which had also suffered from the same cause, were not sufficient for their repair, he made application to many persons of good estate and dignity, and received from them no small moneys for this purpose. Especially did he renew a certain old custom which had fallen into disuse that pious men and women, who could not indeed wholly leave their places in the world and yet were minded to join themselves to the fraternity, should be so admitted. Such did take upon themselves no vows, neither were they bound by any rule, save that of sobriety and temperance which is laid upon all Christian persons; but they were counted to be of the house, and were permitted, on occasion, to vote in the chapter. Whether or no this custom is altogether profitable—as, indeed, what custom is?—I do not pretend to judge; but this is certainly true, that it did bind to the Abbey many friends of great repute and power, and did also no little advantage its revenues; for it is not to be supposed that the persons aforesaid were admitted to such privileges without due acknowledgment made. Thus in the third year of his abbacy the said John of Wheathampstead admitted to the fraternity that most noble Prince Humphrey, Duke of Gloucester, and the Lady Jacqueline of Hainault his wife. And it is recorded that in the eighth year of his abbacy there were so admitted thirty noble persons and more, among whom was Sir Henry Beauchamp, son of the Earl of Warwick.

Thus it came to pass—and this indeed cannot be reckoned as a laudable thing—that the Abbey became more like unto a king's court than a house of God. It is recorded that in the year 1423, being the year of his admission into the fraternity, the said Duke Humphrey kept Christmas at the Abbey, having three hundred men with him. And three years afterwards he came again with a like following, at which time the Abbey was like to have been burned; for when the monks had gone forth to take him on his way to Barnet, the chamber wherein the feast had been served caught fire, and was scarce saved, and that not without destruction of the tapestry wherewith it was hung. In the Easter of this same year came King Henry with Queen Katharine his mother, and was royally entertained for nine days.

After he had filled the Abbot's place for twenty years, John resigned it again into the hands of the brotherhood. But whether he did this from frailty of health (which may be doubted, seeing that he lived thereafter four-and-twenty years), or from weariness of the state and dignity of his office, or, as I myself am inclined to think, because the signs of the time did seem to portend trouble to come, cannot certainly be known. Into the room of the said John the brotherhood choose another, John of Stoke, of whom nothing need here be said; and he having deceased eleven years afterwards, John of Wheathampstead was again chosen, no voice contradicting, and held his place for fourteen years.

This John therefore came in the year of which I am now writing to Gloucester Hall, of which he was always a great favourer, having given, among other things, no small monies for the building of a chapel and a library. He was somewhat infirm of body, being indeed nigh upon fourscore years of age, but vigorous of mind; and one who would not suffer aught to be done where he had authority without his knowledge and consent. I do remember with what weighty speech, with what vigour of gesture and carriage, the old man did tell at table (for I was privileged to sit with the seniors) how in the year before his then coming there had been a great battle in the very streets of St. Albans town, between the army of Queen Margaret and the army of my lord Warwick. "Lord Warwick," he said, "held the town, and when the Queen's men, who were for the most part of the north, had gotten by force of arms to the market cross, for so far they came, his men let fly a great shower of arrows and drave them back. Then the northern men, being driven forth from the town, joined their fellows that were without, and marching to Bernard Heath, where the greater part of my lord Warwick's army was set, fell upon them, and after a very fierce battle put them to flight. Which when they had done they came back to the town, and with no great labour took it. Then the Queen and King Henry with her (for he had been with my lord Warwick upon the field, and had been left by him when he fled) came to the gate of the Abbey, and were straightway admitted. And first they went to the great altar to offer thanks, and then to the shrine of the Saint, and after that—for it was now late and he was weary, being indeed of a feeble habit—to his chamber. But first I besought him on my knees that he would give command to his men that they should not plunder the town. This he did forthwith, sending words to his captains. But this availed nothing, for the men spared nothing whereon they could lay their hands—no, not the poor that have their alms at our gate. And what they took not they wasted, so that the whole countryside was as desolate as the wilderness. But the Abbey they harmed not; and in that, by God's mercy, we had good provision of food, so that when the northerners departed—and this they did in not many days, the Queen having but few friends in those parts and the citizens of London for her chief enemies—we fed the townsfolk, ay, and the countryfolk also, that came to us from many miles round about. But now, God be thanked therefor, we are like to have peace."

After I heard, but the Abbot said nought of the matter, that the prior and the archdeacon and many of the brethren fled from the house during these troubles; so that but for the constancy of the Abbot, affirming that he would not leave the flock of which God had made him overseer, the place had been altogether deserted. The Abbot had speech with me while he tarried at the hall, and after he had inquired of my studies and other matters he said, "If thou art ready, as I doubt not, to take the orders of subdeacon at Whitsuntide next ensuing, after thou shalt go to see thy kindred if thou wilt, and come to the Abbey about the Feast of St. Michael."

But of this time, and of my first coming to the Abbey, and of the year of my noviceship, I will write nothing; for there was, as it were, a great cloud of grief and trouble over me—*"Adhæsit pavimento anima mea."*

OF MY SOJOURN IN THE HOUSE OF ST. ALBANS

THERE is but little change in the life of a monk, save that of nature which bringeth night after day and winter after summer, and that which the Church and our Founder have ordained, commanding that in each year there should be a succession of festivals and fasts, and in each day its due order of services. Neverthelessof one notable thing I may write, seeing that it came to pass in my own time, to wit, the choice of an Abbot. On the 10th day of January, 1464, died John of Wheathampstead, being, as was believed, for no man knew it for a certainty, four-score and one years of age. And on the 25th day of the same month, being the festival of the Conversion of St. Paul, he was buried in a great tomb that he had caused to be built for himself four and thirty years before, so mindful was he, even in the flower of his days, of his latter end. Never was abbot that did more for his house. Of these benefits I will mention the chief, believing that they are his fittest epitaph. He spent

On the buildings of the Abbey	£886
On the Abbot's lodgings	£126
On a mitre and staff	£116
On the Church	£222
On copes, chasubles, and other vestments for the same	£861
On repairs of houses in the town and in the Abbey manors	£1146
On lands that he bought	£1362

And all this he did neither mortgaging any house or manor, nor cutting any timber beyond what was customary, nor pledging any precious thing that was in the treasury.

He greatly increased the library, to which, among many other books, he added Cato *On Rural Matters*, with a glossary, and Boethius *On the Consolations of Philosophy*. He was also a man of no little learning, and in the Latin tongue especially copious, using it with as great an ease as though it were that in which he was born. He was copious also in the making of Latin verses, but careful neither of metre nor of grammar. This is the more to be wondered at, seeing that he was himself well versed, as his epistles do testify, in Ovidius, than whom there is not a better exemplar of verse in the Latin tongue. But indeed I have noted, not once only, that a man in letters, as in other things, may know and approve that which is better, and yet follow after that which is worse.

On the day after the burial was sent a letter to the King, wherein his Grace was informed of the death of John of Wheathampstead, late Abbot, and permission asked that the brotherhood might proceed to the election of a successor. And four days after the said letter, letters were sent to the priors of the cells (that is to say, the smaller houses which do belong to the Abbey) to this purport, that the Abbot had departed this life, and that the election of his successor would be held on the twenty-fifth day of February following, and that their presence on the said day was entreated. On this day therefore there were present seven of the said priors, and all the great officers of the house, that is to say the archdeacon, the almoner, the precentor, the keeper of the shrine, and others, and all the brotherhood, of whom I, having now passed the year of my noviceship, was one. There were forty and four in all. But one brother was sick and languishing in the infirmary; the notary therefore was sent to ask his vote. This done, the notary stood at the door of the chapter-house, and proclaimed with a loud voice: "If there be any other prior or monk that hath a right to vote, let him come forth." After this the Prior said: "If there be any here that shall vote not having the right so to do, he is *ipso facto* excommunicate." This done, the notary read aloud the King's letters whereby the brotherhood had license to elect. And when there had also been read a certain law concerning the election of abbots, the Prior stood up in his place and said, "I, Nicholas Bond, Prior of this house, do name William Alban, doctor in theology, to be father, pastor, and abbot of this church." And when no man spake either to affirm or to deny, the precentor would have begun the *Te Deum*, thanking God that the business had had such quick despatch. But the doctors that were there would not have it so, but commanded that the notary should go round and ask each man singly for whom he gave his voice. And when all with one consent had answered "William Alban," then they bade the precentor to begin the *Te Deum*. This begun, the Prior, and with him the Prior of Tinmouth, being the eldest of the priors of the cells, took William Alban by the hand and led him through the cloister into the choir, and so up to the great altar. There he knelt till the singing of the *Te Deum* was ended. And when it was ended the Prior said to him, "Turn thyself to the people that they may see thee," for the church was filled from the one end to the other. And the eldest of the brethren said, "Hear all ye that are present: William Alban hath been duly and canonically chosen to be father, pastor, and abbot of this church." Then the said William departed to his own chamber, and the rest of the brethren returned to the chapter-house, but the two priors and the archdeacon remained in the church. Thence they sent two proctors to the said William in his chamber asking his consent to the election. The next day the Abbot rode to London that he might be presented to the King and swear fealty. This done he returned, not to the Abbey, but to the country-house of the abbot. Thence, on the day when he should be installed in his place, he rode on horseback, and came to the west door of the church. Here the brethren met him and led him to the choir, and the Prior set him on his throne; and when he had taken the oaths appointed, and the brethren also had sworn obedience, he returned thanks in a set oration. After this he entertained the brethren, with many guests of high degree, at a great feast.

It is very much to be desired, if I may here set down that which is in my secret mind, that there should be some change in the government of this house. Herein I speak not of the interior discipline thereof, but of its dealings with them that are without, and especially with the citizens of St. Albans town. For I have noted, from the time that I first came to this place, that the people are not so kindly affectioned to us as is to be wished. Some will turn out of the way rather than pay the customary reverence, and some of the bolder sort will pass us by without greeting; yea, I have seen one and another spit upon the ground. Now this at the first looking is a marvellous thing; for, as I have heard from them that have the charge of these things, the house dealeth not ungently with the tenants that hold farms and houses and the like, helping them not a little, if by reason of sickness, or murrain among their cattle, or ill harvests, they fail in their payments. And besides this every day there gather a great number of poor and halt and maimed at the Abbey gate (so great indeed is it that they must needs come from the whole country round) who are fed with broken meat. So that none in this town can be in any peril of starving. And if there be any sick in the town the leech of the Abbey is ready to minister to them. These things being so, it is to be looked for that we should be loved rather than hated, and yet it is not so.

And I do begin to understand the cause when I read in the chronicles of this house what hath befallen in these matters in time past, as for example in the chronicle of Thomas Walsingham, some time a monk of this house. I approve not indeed the doings of the townsfolk in the days of Walter Tyler, when they constrained the abbot by force to give up certain bonds and charters and burned them with fire, and did many other things worthy of blame; but, on the other hand, I verily believe that they had many things whereof to complain. For whereas in other places nobles and knights oppressed the commonalty—for how otherwise should they have risen in rebellion—here the very servants of God oppressed them. For it seemeth to me a tyrannous thing, and unworthy of them that are specially bound not to seek their own pleasure or profit, that for the sake of gain they should forbid any man to have so much as a handmill of his own for the grinding of corn, but constrain all the townsfolk to bring their corn for the grinding to the mill of the Abbey. And I marvel not a little that men of God should favour such ill deeds as were done in the name of justice by Sir Robert Tressitian, the Lord Justiciar. For when the jury that he had summoned would not find a true bill against William Gryndecobbe and other persons then accused, he threatened that they should themselves suffer in their stead. Thus he compelled them to find the bill aforesaid. This done, he summoned another jury, and having shown to them the names of them that were so indicted, asked, "What say ye about these men named herein?" And they, supposing that the things were true that were set down by the first jury, answered that they would have judged them to be guilty. And he did in like manner with a third jury also. But the men accused were never brought face to face with their accusers, nor suffered to speak for themselves, nor to make their defence. That they were innocent I say not; but they were condemned as the innocent are wont to be condemned. And it was a horrible thing that the friends and kinsfolk of these men, having carried away their bodies for burial, were compelled to bring them back and hang them again on the gallows with their own hands; and this thing was commanded indeed by the King, but invented, I doubt not, by the Abbot, as it is most certainly approved by the aforesaid Thomas of Walsingham.

I have heard how John the Abbot lately deceased dealt with one William Redhead, a maltster of Barnet town, that was accused to him that he had a certain book of heretical doctrines writ in the vulgar tongue. I excuse not this same William; nevertheless I cannot approve the sentence that was passed upon him by the said Abbot. For it was commanded him that he should once in the year for seven years go barefoot to the shrine of St. Alban the Martyr, and should there offer a wax candle of a pound in weight. This surely had sufficed. Nor did it profit either for the honour of God or for the correction of the wrongdoer that on three several Sundays he should walk naked round the churchyard in his parish of Barnet, and this done should proceed to the high altar and there offer a candle.

It humbleth me much to think of these and such like things, first and chiefly because they do not become them that are bound to be an ensample of charity, humility, and the preferring of others to themselves, but also because they seem to threaten no small peril. For the commons daily grow in power, being especially favoured by the King that now is, who indeed reigneth by their goodwill rather than by the goodwill of the nobles; and that they will continue so to grow I doubt not. And if in time to come we need friends, as they that have great wealth but nought wherewith to guard it will need them of a certainty, where shall we find them, the commons being ill-affected towards us? If the King desire to lay hands upon our possessions (which God forbid!), who shall hinder him if the people be not on our side? Wherefore I desire most earnestly that with the new men there may be, in these things at the least, other manners. But beyond this—and to wish is permitted to all of us, so that we wish not things forbidden—I will not go. I have no hand in the making or mending of such things; and I thank God therefor, for who am I that I should be wiser and better than the holy men who have been with me in this place? I will content myself therefore with doing with all my might whatsoever my hand findeth to do.

I FALL SICK

The 2nd day of April, 1471

I HAD thought to spend the remainder of my days peaceably in this place, where, though there are some things that please me not, and are indeed far other than I hoped—and indeed where are there not such things to be found?—yet a man may, if he will, serve God and his fellows faithfully. But it seems like to be ordered otherwise for me. I have been for some time past troubled with a great weakness of body; and this, not wishing to be burdensome to others, or to be stayed from my work and banished to the infirmary, and thinking that the ailment might cease of his own accord, I kept to myself; but yesterday morning a great giddiness came suddenly upon me at matins, so that I had fallen in my place but that the brethren on either side of me held me up. And when I was led out of the church, it returned yet more violently upon me, so that I fell upon the ground, and so was carried to the infirmary, where I abode for the rest of the day, scarce able to raise my head from my pillow, so feeble was I. Master Philip, the leech, being hastily fetched, cometh, and after brief examination giveth me a cordial, bidding me remain quiet in my place till he should inquire more particularly into my case; and this he said he would do upon the morrow.

This morning accordingly, about half an hour after matins, cometh Master Philip. And when he saw how I fared, for I was by this time not a little relieved, he said, "The Prior must know of thy case, Brother Thomas; and it would be a saving of my time—which is precious, there being no little sickness in the town—if I questioned thee of thyself in his presence. Thou art able," said he, "to walk so far as his lodgings?"

"Yea," answered I; "I slept well, and seem to be much recovered this morning." So we went together to the Prior's lodgings, who indeed had been advertised before of our so coming, if I should be found able. Then said the Prior, "I have noticed for some time past that Brother Thomas here standeth in need of thy ministrations. He is not one of those that hie to the infirmary if so much as their little finger ache, but holdeth fast to his work, concealing his pain, so far as he may. So now do thy best for him, Master Leech, for he is one that will work if only he have the strength." Then the leech questioned me about my ailments, and when he had heard of the giddiness and such like, he said, "Dost eat heartily and with a good appetite? Art thou better content on a flesh day or a fast day?" And when I had confessed that I was wont to eat as little as I might, and further that I oft times vomited after the taking of food, he would further know how I slept. And when he knew that I was troubled with ill dreams, he questioned me further about my manner of life. And when he heard that I was in the *scriptorium* he asked me much about my work, speaking as one that cared for it and desired to know something of it. And when I grew warm in my praises of it, being carried away, as I do now perceive when I remember it, by my love for the work, he went on, "And thou carest little, I take it, for play or sport?" And when I confessed that I had given to my task of writing what time was granted for sleep after dinner, or for walking, and that by special favour of the steward I had had a provision of lights and a small chamber set apart for my use—for in the scriptorium lights are by no means permitted—the good leech held his peace awhile. Then said the Prior, "If Brother Thomas is giddy, as he saith, haply he would be the better for losing some blood." Then Master Philip held up his hands as though he had heard some horrible thing. "Haply there are some in this house who would be the better for such loss, though I hold that two bleedings in the year are as much as the health of most will suffer without damage. But as for this young man, he hath nought to spare: nay, I would put blood into his veins if I could compass it by any art." Then he saith to me, "Tell me how long doth one of the candles that thou hast from the steward serve thee?" "For a matter of six hours," I made answer, "if it be of hard wax." "And how long," he asked further, "if thou burn it at either end at the same time?" "That is past telling," I answered; "but can it be conceived that any man would be so foolish?" "Thou needst not look far for such an one, my son. Nevertheless, thou art not worse than others, and indeed spendest thyself on better things than the most who come to me in their need. But why shouldst thou be more careful of candles of wax than of the candle of thy life? Tell me now, art thou made of other stuff than thy fellows that thou canst live without food or sleep? Now, hearken to me. Thou must not so much as set foot in the *scriptorium*, or read but one line in thy books till I give thee leave. Verily thou hast had enough of books, yea and more than enough, for long time to come; yea, haply for thine whole life." Then he turned to the Prior, and said, "Master Prior, thou wilt take order, I doubt not, that it be as regards the reading or writing of books as I have said. Also I would have the brother excused from all service in the church, except it be matins only. And that his sleep be not broken, let him no longer sleep in the great dormitory here, but have for himself a small chamber in the infirmary. Let him dine with the brethren; but he must be exempted from all fasting, and I will myself, with your good leave, speak to the cook about his diet. And give charge to one of the brethren that he walk at the proper time, and that he be constrained, even against his will, to play at the bowls; and for the rest of his time let the gardener set him to such light tasks in the garden as he can find; and if the weather be foul, let him make nets for the cherry-trees and the strawberries. But as for books, I must tell your lordship these are mere poison to him. And when his health be somewhat mended, as I doubt not that it will if he heed my commands, we will consider further of his case. Some medicine he shall have of me, but the best medicine for such sickness as his, which indeed cometh from over-straining of the mind, is to be found in food and exercise."

Then I departed. What shall be the end of the matter I know not. Verily, if I am to live without books, I had as lief die. Yet why do I murmur against Him that ordereth my ways?

I GO TO LONDON WITH THE KING

The 20tla day of May, 1471.

MANY things have come to pass since I last wrote in this book, things of great moment to this realm, and in which I have taken such a part as was beyond all hope or desire of mine. These I will set down in order according as my memory shall serve.

On the tenth day of April, being the Wednesday before Easter, about six of the clock, my lord King Edward, having with him certain great nobles, of whom his brothers, my lord of Clarence and my lord of Gloucester were the chiefest, and ten thousand men, cometh to St. Albans. The town had but three hours' warning of his coming, which was indeed with much haste, he much desiring to be beforehand with the Earl of Warwick in winning over to his cause the citizens of London. There was much ado therefore about victualling so great a host; nor did the King and his company, who lay in the Abbot's lodging, have such entertainment as could have been desired. On this tenth day of April, after supper, the Lord Abbot sent to me saying that the King would speak with me. And when I was come into the dining-chamber—for the King and his brothers and sundry great lords had supped there, but the knights had supped in the refectory with the brethren—I found the King standing by the fire. A goodly man he is to see—a very Saul among the people, having, as I should judge, six feet and inches three or four of height. His countenance, too, is well-favoured, over full, maybe, and of too deep a red, as of one that hath not always refrained himself at the wine-cup, but finely shaped, for indeed beauty is the heritage of the house of Plantagenet. His hair was as gold, somewhat longer, methought, than beseems a man; and his eyes of as fair a blue as ever I beheld. Then said the Lord Abbot, "Thou seest, Sire, the young man of whom I spake." Then the King turned his regard upon me and said, "Wilt thou with me to the wars, Brother Thomas, if that be thy name, to say mass, and give ghostly comfort to such as need it, for I hear that thy occupation in this place is gone?" "Yea, Sire," I made answer without delay, "with all my heart." "'Tis well spoken," said the King, "few words and of a soldier's fashion, and verily the priest that would follow with the army must be of a soldier's spirit. I trust thou hast not many affairs to settle, for I would have thee set forth with me to-morrow by six of the clock." Then he called to a page that waited at the door, and said, "See that Brother Thomas hath a mule ready for his riding." Then I made my obeisance and departed, the King first crying with a merry voice, "See that thy slumbers be not too long, Brother Thomas, on the morrow." This verily there was small reason to fear; for sleep came not near me all that night. And when the hour of prime was come, I rose, and went to the church, setting at nought the commands of Master Philip, the leech; for I thought to myself that, like enough, what with the danger of sickness that ever followeth hard after war, and such perils of the field as come even to those that mingle not in the fray, I might not enter again into this House of God. And prime being over, I put together in two saddle bags, which a serving man had brought to me, such things as I needed, not forgetting, indeed, that a soldier must endure hardness. Also I put up my *Breviariurn*, the treatise of Boethius, *De Consolatione*, and the *Pharsalicon* of Lucanus, all three being writ in a very small compass with my own hand. These being packed, I carried down to the great gate, where I found already gathered some fifty knights and squires. It wanted then half an hour to six of the clock, as I judged, the sun being newly risen. Presently cometh the King, and his two brothers with him, and certain great nobles also. By this time also the number of the knights and squires was greatly increased, so that there were, as I could best judge, five hundred at the least. And I noted that they were lightly armed, as men that would travel with all the speed that they might. And when the King was mounted he beckoned with the hand that all the company should come close about him. This being done, he spake to this purpose: "My lords and comrades all, I have a purpose in my mind that it is meet for you all to know, for ye must all help therein. Briefly, I will to London with all the speed that may be, for he that hath London hath already, it may well be said, the half of this realm of England. Now ye know that the citizens of London are for the most part well inclined to the House of York; yet there are some rebels among them, and some that favour the Earl of Warwick and Henry of Windsor, under cover of whose name the said Earl doth pretend to rule this kingdom. I count it, therefore, to be no small thing to be beforehand with the said citizens, for the Earl also, as I know for certain, hath the same purpose in his heart. That we have out-marched the said Earl, I doubt not; yet, because so great a matter were best done without delay, I will that we ride to London this day with all speed; and to this end I have bidden you arm yourselves as lightly as may be, that your beasts be not overburdened and weary. Now, there are twenty miles of distance between this town of St. Albans and London. We will draw rein and bait our horses once upon the road; and if our journey be accomplished by noon-day, it shall be well with us, as we shall see. As for the foot soldiers, I have given commandment that they follow us. It shall suffice that they be with us by night-fall. And now, Brother Thomas, give us thy blessing." Then, when I had said the prayer *Pro Militanibus*, with the *Paternoster*, and the *Ave Maria*, and added the *Pax Vobiscuin*, they set forth at a great speed. And though the paces of the mule were easy—and indeed it was the beast of my good friend and brother, the Prior, and lent by him of his great kindness that I should not be troubled with some rough beast out of the camp—because I had been for now six years past unused to riding, I was not a little distressed. Right glad was I when we drew rein at Barnet town, which lieth half-way between St. Albans and London. After this I fared better; and indeed, in my youth, I would ride with the best. So we came to London, the time being close upon noon-day, for so the King had ordered the matter. Now the city was held for King Henry of

Lancaster (for King I must call him, seeing that he hath been duly crowned and anointed, and is beside a right pious prince), by lord of York, brother to the Earl of Warwick, having with him, as I have heard tell, six thousand men-at-arms. Now when we came near to the wall, I saw not thereon so much as a single man in harness, but of men unarmed there was a multitude, and of women not a few. And straightway there opened to us a postern gate, by which the King, having first lighted down from his horse, entered, and his lords after him, I also following the King. There stood one in lawyer's garb that was, as I heard after, Master Thomas Urswyke, the Recorder. Then said the King, "By my faith, but this is passing well done, Master Urswyke. But how hast thou so contrived it?" "Sire, verily I bade the men that kept the wall go home to their dinners, which, indeed, they were nothing loth to do, for our citizens are men of peace, and like not scanty fare." "'Tis well," said the King, "but we will open the great gate and let in my company; for though I may doubt not the good citizens of London, yet I will that they see I come not alone." So the great gate was set open, and the whole company of horsemen came in, and set themselves in fair order on either side of the way. Presently come back the citizens from their dinner, and are not a little astonied to see the array. But when the King espied the captain of the gate—one Master Humblethwaite, as I heard after, a mercer of Aldersgate—he beckoned to him with the hand, that he should come near, and, when he came, whispered something in his ear. Now all this, that I be not overlong in the telling of my tale, had been ordered aforehand. And herein do I perceive proof of that which I have ever heard of my lord the King, to wit, that he is beyond compare the mightiest man of war in all Europe. For a mighty man of war, if a poor monk may write of such things, is not he that can smite the sorest blows with axe or sword, though verily there is not a man-at-arms in this realm that doth excel the King in that which is, as the old Roman hath it, sola militum virtus; nor is he only one that can skilfully set the battle in array, and take the occasions of war as they do arise, though this is, indeed, a great matter; but he must need know everything and remember everything, must forget no man's face, must make himself acquainted with every man's thoughts and wishes. It was thus that the King prospered in the matter of which I write. Verily he had been in great peril, not of his kingdom only, but his life, if he had been shut out from London. Nor was it enough that he had Master Urswyke, the Recorder, for his friend, But he did choose to which gate he should make his approach, remembering that Master Humblethwaite was captain thereof; nor was there one of the chief citizens but that he knew him, whether he was friend or enemy. And when he whispered in Master Humblethwaite's ear, he instructed him, as I heard after from the good citizen himself, whom he should bring out of all the captains of the City bands, choosing not such as were friends only, but also such as might most readily be won over. And so it was that in the space of two hours or less, the great City of London did pass from King Henry to King Edward. Only I did hear that my lord the Archbishop of York was but half-hearted for his brother and the House of Lancaster.

About two of the clock there was a great gathering of citizens, looking very brave in their harness, in the churchyard of St. Paul's; to whom my lord the King made an oration, saying, "Verily, ye men of London, I looked that ye had been more steadfast in my cause. Have ye not ever found me your friend? Have I not confirmed and enlarged your charters? Have ye not had, since first I came to the lordship of this realm, such liberty of trade as your fathers knew not? Think ye that the Earl of Warwick will serve you better? Know ye not that he, and they that follow him, love not the ways of them that dwell in cities, and that, if ye make him your master, he will strip you to the skin?" And more he added to the like effect, yet promised that, seeing they repented them of their error, he would have them in no less favour than before. And when he had made an end there was a great shouting and clapping of hands.

After this the King went into the Church of St. Paul by the north door. Hard by this said door standeth the great rood, than which there is, I take it, no more renowned holy place in this realm of England, save only the tomb of St. Thomas of Canterbury. This rood was found, so say the priests of St. Paul's, in the year of our Lord one hundred and forty by Lucius, that was first Christian King of England. And they say also that many miracles are wrought on sick folk and others at this place; about which things I will say neither yea nor nay. The King made an offering of five gold pieces at the rood; and five other gold pieces he gave for masses for the soul of his father, Richard of York, that was done to death at Wakefield.

'Tis a goodly building this Church of St. Paul; yet I saw in it much that pleased me not. I liked not to see in the nave the twelve tables with scribes sitting thereat, ready to do any manner of worldly business for such as had resort to them. And that which men call Paul's Walk verily pleased me yet less. 'Tis a way by which men pass through the church from north to south, and, save only for the houses, it is as a common street. There were stalls with all manner of merchandise, gay stuffs for men and women's apparel, and ornaments of gold and silver, and the like; and on others there were set forth cakes and confections, yea, and strong liquors, as sherries, sacks, and hippocras, for such as desired them. And the men and women that served the stall cried, "Come buy," loudly and instantly to them that passed. And other traders of the poorer sort walked to and fro with baskets on their heads, making advertisement of their goods without regard for the place. And the people that passed to and fro talked and laughed, as they had been in the open street, not keeping themselves even from evil words, for I heard profane oaths, and that not once or twice only. And verily, for this is a thing that is scarcely to be believed, I saw one that had a cross-bow in his hand, and he shot at a pigeon that flew down from the north tower. Of a truth the citizens of London have made of this House of God a *spelunca latronum*.

From the church the King goeth to the Bishop's house, which standeth at the west end of the nave on the northern side. Here he findeth King Henry and the Archbishop of York, left, as I heard say, of all their company. And when he had lodged these for safe custody in the Tower, he went by water to Westminster; and so, after giving of thanks in the Abbey, to the Palace. As for me, I lodged that night and the next in the Abbot's house.

It skills not to tell how the next day was spent; war taketh no account of seasons, and, after matins, which I myself said by the King's commandment in the Lady chapel, there was no word or thought but of battle. The King's army lay, for the most part, without the city, along the road by the which we had ridden on the day before, for by this same he was minded to return without delay, knowing that the Earl of Warwick was following hard after him. But he was minded to add thereto as great a company of citizens as he could gather together. Therefore was there all that day a great going to and fro of aldermen and deputies, and other great folk from the city. As for the Lord Mayor, he was sick, or feigned himself to be so; and his deputy had fled. But the greater part of the rich merchants and men of substance spared nothing in the King's cause, having, I do verily believe, a true favour towards him, and also because he owed them much money which they should lose if he prospered not. Many money bags did they bring, and there was a great gathering of arms and artillery, the finest that could be got. The young men also willingly offered themselves to serve in arms. The most of them were bowmen and billmen, but some were men-at-arms. Also there gathered to the King many knights and squires that had been in hiding from the day that he fled, or had feigned to take sides against him.

OF THE BATTLE OF BARNET

ON the morrow, being Easter Eve, about one hour after noon, the King set forth, marching northwards, by the same road by the which he had come. And about four of the clock we came to Barnet, which is a small town with a market, about ten miles from London, lying for the most part on a hill that slopeth southward and eastward, and on the top of the hill there is a lair plain. It was now close upon sun setting, and there was such a mist as I have never seen at any time. Already when we set forth from London it had begun to rise from the earth; and now, as we came nigh to Barnet town, it was so thick that a man could scarce see a spear's length before him. This, it was commonly reported, was brought about by the enchantments of one Bungay, a Black Friar. This I can scarce believe, for I doubt whether any man hath power by charms and such like to change the course of nature, though, indeed, it was credited among the ancients that the witches of Thessaly could make the moon dark by their enchantments. The likelier cause, methinks, was this, that the earth being wet with much rain, there came a sudden heat of the sun (and such, indeed, there was for the three days next before this Saturday of which I write), and that the mist was begotten of the heat and rain together. But be the cause what it might, so much is certain, that it favoured the King greatly. I pretend not to have knowledge of warlike matters, but I have talked with many that have such; and I understand not for what cause, save only it was the hindering of this mist, my lord of Warwick and the Marquis Montagu, being right skilful commanders, suffered the King to bring his army without let up the hill of Barnet to the plain that lieth upon the top. They were content to take but half of the said plain, having it in their power to take the whole, for that they were beforehand with the King by five or six hours at the least. Why brought they not their host to the very edge of the hill so that they might have hindered their adversaries in the climbing thereof, for it is a steep place, and they that stand upon the top have no small advantage over them that ascend? To this question I have no answer, save that for this thickness of the air they knew not where they stood. Certes the King was greatly profited by the mist in this matter, and in others also of which I shall presently speak. Having, therefore, ascended the hill without hindrance, and passed through Barnet town, he made his encampment on the plain hard by, not suffering his men to abide in the said town. And because he had marched out in haste, with as little baggage as might be, the soldiers fared, as best they might, without tents, comforting themselves with fires; only there was a pavilion pitched for King Henry, which the King carried with him. And before the army there were dug trenches, and palisades were fixed in the earth, lest the enemy should take them at unawares in the night. And now I will make mention of another thing in which, as I have said, the mist served the King. For he, thinking to set his army in array over against the enemy, but not knowing truly where they lay, did extend his right wing too far towards a great wood which is in these parts, and which men call the Chase of Enfield. So it came to pass that his left wing was withdrawn from the right of the enemy, and thus escaped no small loss. For in this said right wing were certain cannon, from which great bullets of lead were shot forth by force of gunpowder, which bullets had done great damage, but that they fell upon an empty space. And so did the mist serve the King a second time, and that by his own error, so wonderful are the ways of God towards man. These cannon made a terrible great noise, yet were they scarce heeded that night, for the whole plain was in an uproar, so that, what for neighing of horses and talking of men, none in either host could get any rest or quietness.

But how shall I, that am a man of peace, set forth in words the battle that followed upon the next day, which, indeed, was Easter Day. It being now more than a month past the equinox, the day began to break about four of the clock; nor was there any delay on either side, but all addressed themselves to the fight, so weary were they of waiting. And when the captains of the two hosts had set their battle in array as best they could for the scantiness of the light, then King Edward on the one side, and my lord of Warwick on the other, gave such exhortation to their men as time permitted. What the Earl of Warwick spake I know not of my own knowledge, nor will I write it down from the report of others; but the words of the King I heard with my own ears. He bade the soldiers fight valiantly as knowing that their cause was just and was surely favoured of God. "They that have set themselves in array against you this day have not only broken their oaths to me, which were of itself in comparison a small thing, but are traitors to the realm and spoilers of the poor commonalty, which I and my house have holpen, yea, and will always help to the utmost of our power, and are people destitute of all grace, good fortune, and good living. And if these mischievous persons should prevail this day through the faintness of your hearts, know ye for a surety that it shall fare ill with all. Such of you as are gentlemen and rich men shall be in jeopardy, not only of the spoiling of your goods, but also of your lives, seeing that they who take to themselves the riches of others count not themselves secure in their possessions till they have taken their lives also. Ye are that of meaner estate will assuredly suffer robbing and spoiling, especially ye that dwell in towns and cities, and are concerned with buying and selling both at home and beyond the seas, for Warwick and the nobles that are with him love not traders. And as for you that are peasants and handicraftsmen, for you they design perpetual bondage and servitude, desiring, above all things, to take from you that freedom which ye have. Think not that these great lords are lovers of freedom; so that they be free themselves to do what they list, they care not for aught else. Trust ye rather to your King, inasmuch as he knoweth that whoso ruleth over free men is greater than he that ruleth over slaves. Bear yourselves, therefore, with a brave heart; and, seeing that this realm hath had enough, yea, and too much, for many years past of civil war, so strike that after this day ye shall not need to strike again."

It hath, I know, been commonly reported that the King gave commandment to his soldiers that they should not spare their adversaries even when these should have yielded themselves. Yet such meaning may not fairly be drawn from his words, which need not intend anything further than an exhortation to valiant doing. But what the captains said each to their own men I know not. This only I know, that the battle was fought with much rage and fury on either side; as, indeed, was like to be when the battle was between brothers, if I may say so; and that some, beyond doubt, were ruthlessly slain who would in common times have been kept alive either for pity's sake or for ransom.

About five of the clock the trumpets sounded for the attack, and the King's army moved forwards. But whither they were moving, and with whom they were about to contend in battle, this they could scarce see. For though the mist would lighten for the space of a few minutes, yet would it grow thick again, and though it would well-nigh pass from one place or another, yet in no long time it would roll back, wrapping all things in obscurity. At the first, therefore, if I may so speak, there was not one battle, but many. For the soldiers fought not according to the plans and counsels of their leader, but rather contended against their enemies in companies of ten and companies of a hundred, so that there was not one line of battle, but a line broken into many parts. First the archers shot their arrows amidst the enemy, and after the archers came the billmen, and after the billmen the men-at-arms and knights, but these last very slowly and cautiously, for they feared to fall into a snare.

Now at the first it seemed like that the King would suffer defeat. For the right wing of my lord of Warwick's army having a great advantage in numbers, and being led also by two most brave and skilful captains—to wit, the Marquis Montagu and the Earl of Oxford—fell upon the left wing of the King's army and brake it and drave it back, so that it fled, seeking refuge in the houses of Barnet town and in the great wood of Enfield Chase, which lieth to the eastward of the town. And some of them that fled, or, as others will have it some that stood by and watched the battle rode with all the speed of their horses to London, and told, to the no small fear of the citizens, how that the King's army was altogether broken. And now mark again how the mist saved the King's cause. For whereas had the day been clear, all the host would doubtless have suffered much discouragement seeing how their comrades fled, now, by reason of the darkness, scarce any knew of the thing so that they fought with as good a courage a though no ill chance had befallen them. And now the good success of the adversaries turned as often happeneth in war time, to their damage. For some of the soldiers pursued them that fled into the wood, and others fell to plundering the houses in Barnet town Thus was much time spent in vain; and when their captains had painfully gathered together such as they could find (but some returned not at all), lo! another mischance. For coming back to the field of battle by way of Barnet town they came face to face with the middle part of' the army of the Earl of Warwick. Now in this middle part, whereof the Duke of Somerset; was captain, were set the archers. And these, thinking not that they who came from the southward were friends (for by this way had come the army of the King), and not discerning their faces, some of which had else been known to them by reason of the mist, the archers, I say, let fly a shower of arrows upon them. And for this error there was also, I have heard tell, another cause. For King Edward's men had upon their coats a sun with rays streaming therefrom, and the men of the Earl of Oxford a mullet—that is to say, a star with five points—which two things had a close similitude, and could scarce be discerned except by them that looked closely. Thus again did the mist serve King Edward, causing his enemies to fall by the hands one of another. And so it was that when the archers let fly upon them, my lord Oxford's men thinking that they were betrayed—and indeed in those days a man could scarce know for a certainty who were his friends and who his enemies—cried, Treachery! treachery! and fled from the field, as did also their leader.

Then, while the archers doubted what this might mean, and some of them also looking more closely at those that had fallen by their arrows saw that they were indeed friends, then fell no little fear upon them, and they wavered to and fro, not knowing whether they should go forward or fall back. Which when King Edward perceived, for he was close at hand, he cried to them that followed him that the time was come, and that God had delivered their adversaries into their hands. Now at the beginning certain companies both of horsemen and footmen, having indeed a greater host than be could conveniently set in line, he had reserved. To these he now gave command that they should join the battle. And this they did, and because they had not wearied themselves with fighting, but were refreshed with food and drink, they bore down their adversaries before them; for these were spent with toil and hunger, having fought for three hours and more, and this, for the most part, fasting. But the Earl of Warwick on his part had none such on whom he could call. As for King Edward, he bore himself that day with such courage—nay, if I may so say, with such fury—that it seemed as if none could withstand him. And indeed he had such strength and stature as could scarce be matched in either army. Nor, indeed, did my lord of Warwick and they that were with him fail to quit themselves like men. So much I heard afterwards from them that had been near them, both friends and foes. But I say not aught of them, because I speak only of that which I saw with mine own eyes. And now it could scarce be doubted what the issue of the day should be; for the line of Lancaster was broken. Nevertheless the battle was not yet ended, for in one place and another there were some that yet held out, holding their lives cheap, as men oft times do in the heat and fury of fighting, or, it may be, not knowing that their, companions had fled, for the mist was yet thick over the field though the sun was now high in the heavens. But these also were overborne one by one, so that by an hour before noon the battle was ended. And about noon there sprang up a wind from the west, and scattered the mist, so to speak, in a moment of time, and showed the whole plain. I pray God that I may never see such a sight again; and indeed it was such as even the men of war could scarce look upon without shrinking of heart. For though there have been slain in other battles of these last wars more by many times (as at the battle of Hexham there fell of the vanquished alone eight and twenty thousand, but at Barnet of both armies not many more than three thousands), yet here the dead lay together in a small space. The cause whereof was this, that the mist had kept them that fought together, none knowing where or among whom he might find himself if he should move from his place. And even as they fought so did they fall, so that for the space of two or three furlongs was the ground, which, as I have before written, is here a plain upon the top of a hill, was covered with dead bodies both of men and horses. And these lay in all manner of ways, some decently composed as though they slept, and others, wrested, if I may so say, out of all shape, as though they had been wracked with pains that could scarce be borne. And it seemed to me that the sight was even more dreadful to behold because of the bright shining of the sun; for indeed, now that the mist was driven away by the wind, the heavens were clear and without a cloud. Nor indeed did I fail to remember that this day of slaughter was the Feast of the Resurrection of Our Lord, than which there should be, by rights, no more joyful day in the whole year. But of this few, it seemed to me, took any account. For the ill creatures that hang ever upon the skirts of an army, and find their prey, like unto the vultures, among the dead, had come forth seeking to spoil the dead, yea, and I do verily believe, sparing not, if occasion served, to slay the wounded. And some, that were not so wicked as these, yet were careless and hard of heart, did wander over the field, as though they saw some curious spectacle, but gave no help to any that needed. And among the conquerors, for the King halted upon the plain till his men had taken their noonday meal, there was laughter and singing, but not such mirth, I trow, as becometh the feast-day of the Lord.

OF CERTAIN THINGS AFTER THE BATTLE OF BARNET

AS for myself I was busied that day, and indeed not that day only, with my priest's office. What I did while the battle yet raged in its fury I cannot tell even if I would, for the dying were carried without ceasing to where I stood in the rear of the King's army—and there were other priests with me, to wit, the parsons of East Barnet and of Chipping Barnet and of South Mimms, and another whom I knew not—and there I shrived, and if time served, delivered the sacraments, but to whom I gave them I cannot remember, save only that the Lord Cromwell, son of my lord of Essex, and of near kin to King Edward, was among them. He died in the space of about an hour, having been sorely wounded by a lance in the right side, and was buried, I have heard, in the Abbey of Westminster. But one matter which I do remember I will relate, for it is noteworthy. About eleven of the clock, the battle being but just ended, there cometh a serving-man in a black habit, without arms, and holding a white flag in his hand, crying, "Is there here a priest?" And when I had said that I was such, he said, Wilt thou come where there is need of thee?" And at that instant it chanced that the King, for he was standing nigh, having lighted down from his horse, looked towards us. Now he, I have heard say, remembereth every face that he hath seen—which is often the wont of kings and other great folk—and he said to the serving-man, "Surely thou art body servant to the Earl of Warwick?" And the man answered, "Yea, my lord, if indeed he liveth, for I left him at the point to die. Wilt thou of thy Christian charity suffer this priest to see him?" And the King said to me, "Go with all speed, for I would not that my worst enemy should lack spiritual help in his need, and verily Lord Warwick was once my good friend." So I went with the serving-man, it might be the space of half a mile or thereabouts. Then, under a great tree (it was an elm, I mind me, and the leaves were partly grown and small, so that the sun shone through them), I came upon the Earl, and by him certain of the King's soldiers, for his own followers had fled for their lives. His head was uncovered, and his face deathly pale, and his eyes shut, so that I could scarce believe that he yet lived; but when his servant put a cordial to his mouth, he opened his eyes. Then as I drew near he said, but so as I could scarce hear him, "My brother." And the serving-man made as though he would say that he was dead, for so much I understood from the moving of his lips. Thereupon I answered, "He is at peace." For the Marquis Montagu lay dead hard by. Then the Earl said, "It is well. And now I will make confession." So I beckoned with the hand to them that stood by that they should go back a space. Then he made his confession, very brief, for the time was short; and indeed I had scarce said *absolvo te* when he died. God have mercy on his soul! A great prince he was, and of a noble spirit. Temperate he was, and of a cleanly life, and his hand was ever open to the poor, nor was he covetous of wealth; but of power he could have never enough.

After these things I returned to my place. And the King, who was now ready to depart—for he returned to London that same afternoon said to me, "How fares it with the Earl?" And I answered, "He is dead." "And the Marquis Montagu?" "He was dead before my coming." Then the King seemed somewhat moved, and indeed he had always loved the Marquis the better of the two brethren. After he said to one of them that stood by, "See that their bodies have no hurt, and let their kinsfolk bury them where they will" (and this was done at the Abbey of Bisham-by-Thames, hard by Marlow town). And to me, "Stay thou here, where there be many that need thy help; and after return to thy abbey, where thou shalt hear somewhat from me anon." After this he departed, having first given charge of our welfare to a certain John Borrett, an armourer of the City of London, yet dwelling in the manor-house of Thomas Frowyke. Master Borrett would have had me to dine with him, and indeed it was full late, being already past one of the clock, but there came a messenger from the chaplain of Hadley, saying that he desired my presence. And when I went I found the chapel, which is small and almost ruinous, filled with wounded men. And the chaplain, though indeed he was not the chaplain, but a deputy only, was in great strait. He was a brother of the Abbey of Walden, in Essex, which is a House of the Benedictines (for Hadley belongeth to Walden), and a young man, newly ordained to the priesthood, that had not, for so he said, before heard a confession. Willingly therefore did I render him such help as I could. Of these wounded four died before sunset. The others were disposed in the houses of certain charitable inhabitants; but one could not be moved, so sorely wounded was he, but remained perforce in the chapel till the Tuesday in Easter, when he also departed this life. Among them that died was one Peter Le Sueur, a squire of Ghent, in Flanders, with whom, because he could speak no English, I held converse in the Latin tongue, in which he was indifferently well versed. He had followed, for so he said, the Duke of Exeter to the battle, and he made entreaty to me that I would serve the Duke, if by any means I could. "For," said he, "I think that he still liveth. That he was not wounded to the death I know, for we fell together, and having some slight skill in surgery, I bound up his hurt, which was in the outer part of the thigh. And he hath a servant, or one that was a servant in time past, dwelling in these parts, who is faithful to him (as indeed he should be, for the Duke is a noble prince). But what hath befallen him I know not, for they carried me to this place, but him they left, thinking, haply, that he was dead." To him I made answer that I was but a brother of St. Albans, and had no power nor wealth, but would give the Duke such help as I could.

I doubted much if I could do aught in the matter; nevertheless by chance, or, I should rather say, by the good ordering of God, there came in my way an occasion of rendering the Duke some service. For that same night as I sat after supper with Master Borrett the armourer, with whom, as I have before written, I lodged, the talk fell upon the said Duke after this manner. Saith Master Borrett," 'Tis strange that I, being by trade a maker of arms, should mislike war. But, in truth, I never thought so ill of it as I have this day and yesterday. The citizens of London have ever favoured, as haply thou knowest, the cause of King Edward, for the King favours the commons against the nobles, and in time past when I was a captain in the train-bands, I have even struck a blow for his Grace. Therefore was I ill at ease when yesterday cometh my lord Warwick with an army, not knowing how I should fare. The women folk indeed I sent away now a month since, and they are safe at my house in Eastchepe, but I myself was minded to abide and put as bold a face on the matter as I could. So soon, therefore, as the Earl was come to Barnet plain, I made myself ready to get speech with him. And when I was admitted to his presence I said that my poor house was at his disposal if he would lodge therein himself or dispose there any of his captains. And he thanked me, being a courteous prince, though indeed he could, had he chosen, have taken all that I had by force. So it was ordered that my lord of Exeter, with his following, that is to say, two knights and four esquires, should lodge with us. And so it was; nor indeed could I have found better had I been free to choose out of all the host. For the Duke bore himself with all kindness and courtesy, as did also the knights and esquires in their degree, for indeed there is not a truer proverb than *Like master, like man*. I had talk with him about foreign parts, especially about Flanders, in which country he hath sojourned of late, and about the following of my own trade in those parts, of which matter he hath no small knowledge. Nor did I favour him the less because he hath John of Gaunt to his great-grandfather." When he said so much my good host brake off his speech and was silent for a space. Then he said, "I am not one of those who can keep silence of that which is in their hearts; and I hope also (but how I know not, for thou hast not touched on the matter) that to thee I may speak safely. Thou knowest that John of Gaunt was a favourer of Master John Wiclif, who, though I hold not with all that he taught, was, I take it, a true servant of God. And it was of him and his protection that Master John was saved from the fire, and endured not while yet alive that which after his death was done to his bones. Wherefore I hold the said John of Gaunt and all his kindred in honour, and would gladly serve one of his house if occasion should offer. As for the Duke, whether he be dead or alive, I know not. For so soon as he and his company were gone forth in the morning—and this they did before break of day—I drew up the bridge, suffering none to go forth from my house till the battle should be ended. And when one of my hinds brought me tidings that the victory was with King Edward, I issued forth; but of the Duke I have neither seen nor heard aught." Then I stretched forth my hand to him and said, "Of Master Wiclif we will speak, if time shall serve, hereafter. Let it now suffice to say that herein thou hast judged rightly of me. Thou shalt have no ill word of me because thou honourest him. But now as to the Duke I have somewhat to say," and I told him how that I found Peter Le Sueur in Hadley Chapel, and what the young man had said to me. Then said Master Borrett, "I noted the young man that he had an honest and kindly look, but I could not talk with him. It troubleth me to hear that he is dead. But now as to the Duke. That there is one dwelling in these parts who was servant to him before he was banished, I know. 'Tis one Ruthland, and he dwelleth some six furlongs hence on the right hand of the way as thou goeth to South Mimms. Maybe, if the Duke, as thou sayest, was not slain outright in the battle, he is in hiding in John Ruthland's dwelling. But more of this hereafter. I will consider myself what had best be done. Meanwhile 'tis the hour of sleep, which, if thou be like unto me, thou must by this time sorely need." So he took me to my chamber, a fair room and well furnished. And that night I dreamt not, as I had feared, of that which I had seen and heard that day, but of things long past, being again, in my fancy, a scholar of Eton College.

The next day the country folk there round about dug two great trenches wherein to bury the dead, putting them of the King's part in one, and those of the Earl's part in the other. And the parsons and chaplains of the neighbouring parishes said the appointed prayers over them, taking them by fifties and by hundreds, in which pious work I also did my part.

The next day, being the Tuesday in Easter, saith Master Borrett the armourer to me, "I hear from one of my hinds that there is certainly some in hiding in the house of John Ruthland. 'Tis very like that 'tis the Duke. Canst thou get speech with him, thinkest thou? They will trust thee rather than me, who am known in these parts as a favourer of the King." And this I said that I would do. So the next day being market-day (for buying and selling will go on though the world be turned upside down), I lay in wait, so to speak, for John Ruthland at a certain place in the road where none were like to note our meeting. And when he came by I saluted him, making signs that I would speak with him.

I noted that his regard was somewhat troubled and fearful, but he did not refuse to tarry. Then I said, "Tell me, if thou wilt, how one should go to the priest's dwelling at South Mimms." And when he had told me, I asked him two or three questions more of persons and places thereabouts, to which, when he had answered as briefly as courtesy permitted, he said, "Pardon me, father, but business presseth, and I must away." Then I said, "Tarry yet one moment. Dost thou know one Peter Le Sueur?" And before he could answer—for I saw that he was greatly troubled—I said, "I am a friend, and one that may be trusted," and so told him that which I had heard in the Chapel of Hadley. Thereupon he said, "Father, it seemeth to me that I have no choice but to trust thee. May God deal so with thee as thou dealest with the Duke, for indeed he is in hiding at my house." Then I told him of Master Borrett's good-will, and it was agreed between us that he should come after nightfall to the house and take counsel with him. And when he was come, saith Master Borrett, "I have considered the matter with myself, and my thought is this. To order things so that the Duke should escape beyond seas were a hard matter and a perilous; nor indeed could I answer to my lord the King if one of his enemies should pass by my help to some place where he could again conspire against him. But there is at Westminster a sanctuary to which if he can but win, he shall be safe. Now I have a waggon which passeth over the road between Barnet town and London once or twice in the month. 'Tis well known for mine, and I am known for a favourer of the King; so that I doubt not it will go without question. The Duke shall ride therein, clothed as a serving-man, and, for more safety, shall feign to be sick. But say, Master Ruthland, how doth he fare in' health?" Saith he, "I have not had the leech to him, for this is a secret which is best in the keeping of as few as may be. But my good dame hath some skill in dealing with wounds, and she adviseth me that he is doing well. But he can scarce travel for seven days or so." "That is small loss," said Master Borrett;

"this week, I doubt not, they will watch the sanctuary with much diligence, but the next they will slacken their care. But do thou bid the Duke be of a good courage, for that things will doubtless go well with him."

And so indeed it fell out. On the twenty fourth day of April I came back to the Abbey, and four days after cometh Master Borrett and had speech with me in the strangers' parlour. Saith he, "All went well as a man could desire. On the morrow after thy departing I sent the waggon, and with it the Duke clothed as a serving-man. And this day I chose because it was a holiday, being the Feast of St. Mark. As I did suppose, there was no question asked on the road. And indeed for greater safety I did myself travel with the waggon, thinking also that if discovery should be made, I being present might the better excuse my own part in the matter. So being arrived in London about eleven in the forenoon, we had dinner at my house in Eastchepe. And after dinner we went by water from the Bridge where indeed I have my own boat, to Westminster, the Duke being still habited as a serving-man—and for better concealment he had shaved his lip. Now I had so ordered the time of our going that the folk were even then gathering for Evensong. With these we past into the church, the Duke walking heavily, as one that was yet feeble. And I said to a verger of my acquaintance, 'Let us in, I pray, by a private door, for the man is sick, and would make a vow for his health's sake at the shrine of the Confessor.' And this he did. More I cannot tell thee, for I judged it well to leave him at the shrine, having indeed done what I could. But the next day it was noised abroad in London that the Duke of Exeter had taken sanctuary, and that the King had promised him his life, confirming it by an oath. I pray God that it, may, go well with him."

At this present I have nothing more to write, but wait for what shall happen. But I do pray with all my heart that it be not such as hath befallen me, of late. There are yet wars and rumours of wars in the land, and the King, with his brothers of Clarence and Gloucester, goeth westward with an army.

Friday, the tenth day of May, 1471.

Though I be not a chronicler of the affairs of the realm, yet do I feel constrained to set down the tidings which have been just now brought to the abbey, that on Saturday there was fought a great battle at Tewkesbury in which the King did altogether vanquish his adversaries, that the Prince Edward, whom some call Prince of Wales, was slain, but whether in the battle or after the battle, seemeth to be doubtful; that the Duke of Somerset, and other nobles with him, were taken and beheaded; also that Queen Margaret was taken prisoner. And it was told also that before the armies joined battle the Duke of Somerset did slay with his own hand the Lord Wenlock, whom he did suspect of drawing back from the fight. As at Barnet it was treachery, or the fear of treachery, that brought the Earl of Warwick to ruin, so has it been with his friends and companions at Tewkesbury. Verily it is true that a house divided against itself falleth.

The fifteenth day of May, 1471.

This day came news that the Bastard of Falconberg sailing up Thames with a fleet of ships, landed at Blackwall, and thence marched upon the City; which for a time he seemed like to take, but the citizens were staunch, and so drave him back to Stratford in the county of Essex; that on Monday, the thirteenth of this month, he came again near to the walls with a great host of peasants, but hearing that the King was at hand with his army; fell back upon his ships, and so departed. The messenger also said that the King rode into London before his army on Tuesday, and that the same evening it was noised abroad that King Henry was dead. And the cause, 'twas said, was his vexation and displeasure, but there were some that whispered that he was done to death by the King's command. On this matter I say nothing save this, first, that men have ever been suspicious about the deaths of princes, more especially if such have had any notable opportuneness of time; and second, that King Henry had of a certainty suffered such vexation as might well have ended his' life. What hath he not endured in loss of fortune and friends, and scorn and contumely, from the day, now nineteen years past, when I and my companions did see him in his garden at Windsor! God rest his soul, for he was a pious prince, though indeed most unhappy, and who give peace to this realm, which hath suffered such misery as no man can write. Of the nobles, two parts at the very least have perished either in the field or on the scaffold; and the land hath been wasted with fire and sword, so that no small portion of it lieth desolate and without increase; and the merchants are impoverished with loans and benevolences; and even the Church lands are sorely burdened with mortgages. 'Tis a bloody ending that there hath been to these troubles; but if so be 'tis an ending, men, for the most part, will be satisfied.

OF THE CHANTRY OF BARNET

The sixth day of June, 1471.

I HEARD this day of Master Brown of Colney, that my lord the King is minded to build a chantry on Barnet Field. Master Brown holdeth a water-mill and certain meadows of the Abbey, and came hither, as is the custom, ten weeks or thereabouts after the Feast of Our Lady, to pay his dues, certain sacks of wheat and ten marks in money, for the half-year last past. I have some knowledge of him, having been sent for in haste to minister the sacraments to his father now deceased, the parson of Colney lying dead in his house of the spotted fever, and the man hath kindly thoughts of me for such service as I did to him and his. His story was in this wise: "I was in Barnet yesterday with a certain baker with whom I have dealings in the way of my trade, whose house is over against the Crown hostelry, which doubtless thou knowest, having tarried in Barnet when thou wast with the King. And as we sat, our business being ended, over a flagon of ale, we were ware of a goodly company of horsemen that drew rein at the door of the said hostelry, to whom came forth Master Richard the host, cap in hand, bending low as to travellers of great worship. Then said master baker, 'On my life 'tis the King and none other.' I scanned him well, and indeed he is a goodly person, though somewhat overgrown. And those two that favour him so greatly are his brothers of Clarence and Gloucester. We noted that when the King had spoken certain words to the host there ran a little lad as one that carried a message with all haste. Presently, the riders sitting meanwhile on their horses, the lad came back, and in no great space of time there followed him Sir Thomas Aston, that is parson of Barnet. With him the King had some speech, and after the whole company rode forwards, going towards the Field, but at a foot's pace, the parson walking with them covered, for the King would have it so, as we saw by the gesture of his hand. Then said master baker, 'Let us e'en follow these great folk and learn wherefore they be come.' And though I was loath to meddle in that which concerned me not, yet he overbore me, and I went. There followed also no small concourse of the townsfolk. And when the King and his company were come to the open space which lieth to the north of Barnet town they turned somewhat to the left hand, where, three hundred yards or thereabouts from the highway, there standeth a clump of fir trees. There did the King and they that were with him light down from their horses, and, having uncovered, knelt for a space, and we that had followed stood on the highway, for the parson had beckoned to us with the hand that we should not approach nearer. Then the King rose up, and after he had talked for a space with Master Aston, he mounted upon his horse, as also did his company. Then sticking spurs, they rode northward, minding, as one told me afterwards, to visit Master More, who hath a fair house in North Mimms. And while I tarried, noting such tokens of the battle as yet remained upon the field—broken pieces of horses' reins and bits and other trappings and the like (but all that was price the Barnet folk had gathered, aye, and made a good market thereof, and with them, and I doubt not, of some things that had not been in this or any battle), came up Master Aston and greeted me full courteously. 'Would'st thou hear news,' saith he, 'Master Brown, for this, methinks, is no secret of state? My lord the King is minded to build him a chantry where a priest may sing the mass day by day for the souls of them that were slain on Barnet Field. Didst thou note the place where he and his company knelt upon the ground? There first, as the King said to me with his own mouth, did my lord Warwick's men give ground, and there will he have it built, a fair chapel and a lodging for a priest. Truly I had been better pleased had he added it to my own church of Barnet; but 'tis a good work, howsoever it be done; and I misdoubt me,' this he said whispering lest any perchance should overhear, 'whether all the King's revenue be as well spent.'" After this Master Brown departed. Truly I am rejoiced that God hath put it into the King's heart, which seemeth over much set on worldly things, thus to give thanks for his deliverance.

The Feast of St. Barnabas, 1471.

I thought not that Master Brown's tidings which he told me, now five days since, touching the chantry that should be built on Barnet Field, concerned me so nearly. But this morning there cometh a letter from the King to my lord the Abbot, which letter I will here transcribe.

"To the Right Reverend Father in God, my right entirely beloved counsellor, William Abbot of St. Albans, Greeting—

"I have it in my mind for the glory of God, and for the encouragement of good faith and honesty among men, to build a chantry on Barnet Field, in which a priest shall sing mass day by day for the souls of the Lord Cromwell, the Lord Say, Sir Humphrey Bourchier, and of all others that were slain in the battle of Barnet on my party. And I will that there be paid to the said priest one shilling by the day, the said priest promising for his part, if he be hindered by sickness or any other cause, to provide some one of good repute to sing mass in his stead. And I will that one Thomas Aylmer, at this present a brother in your Abbey of St. Alban, have this office, so that your lordship give consent, the said Thomas Aylmer having companied with my army in the same battle, and done good service ministering to them that were wounded and like to die, and otherwise approved himself good and faithful. And because, though I have laid my command on Master William, my chief builder, that he build the said chantry with a convenient lodging for the priest without delay, there must needs be no small space of time before the work be finished, I will that the said Thomas Aylmer begin to sing mass, as here aforesaid, in the Parish Church of Barnet on the Feast of St Peter next ensuing. And I will that, till the said chantry any lodging be built, he receive the sum of four pence by the day, over and above the said sum of one shilling, out of which he shall pay to the parson of Barnet two pence for the use of his church and of the vessels of the altar. I pray that God have you in His keeping; and so farewell.

"Given at my Court of Westminster, this tenth day of June in the year of our Lord, 1471.

"EDWARD R."

Verily I am thankful to my lord the King that he hath such kind remembrance of my, poor services on Barnet Field. And though I be loath for some reason to leave this Abbey of St. Alban, than which there is not, I trow, in the whole realm of England, a fairer house of God, and in which also I had some time hoped to end my days; yet I do think that I see the hand of God in this matter. For I doubt me much whether, if I abide here, I shall have strength to follow that on which my heart is chiefly set, the writing out of books (Master Thomas, the leech, has not suffered me so much as to set foot in the *scriptorium*). I doubt also, however this may be, whether this art of the writing out of books may not come to an end (such strange things do I hear of this new device of printing). There is another cause, also, why I should be not unwilling to depart, of which it beseemeth me to write little. There are certain in this place that walk disorderly, of whom I will at this present say no more than that I pray to God that they may speedily mend their ways.

OF MY MANNER OF LIFE AT BARNET

The Feast of St. Peter, 1471.

THIS day I sang mass for the first time in the church of Barnet. But I should say that the priest of Barnet, when he heard of my coming, constrained me to lodge with him till my own dwelling should be built. And this I did right willingly; but I also constrained him on my part to take somewhat of me for my lodging and food, knowing that he was a poor man (for he had not a church of his own, but is deputy only to the priest of East Barnet), and having also a good provision by the bounty of the King. So I persuaded him, but not easily (and I have noted that the poor are oftentimes hospitable even above their means, and that the rich are not less grudging), that he should take from me two shillings by the week, beside that which I did pay him day by day, according to the King's letter, for the using of the church.

There is one thing which it were ill done of me not to set down in this place. Yestereven, when it was just about to grow dark, there came to the priest's lodging one asking for me by name. And when I went forth to speak with him, I perceived that he was the serving-man that had come on Barnet Field to fetch me to the Earl of Warwick, his master. When he had saluted me he said, "Sir Edward, thou art to sing mass, men say, by the King's command, for the souls of them that fell fighting on his party on Barnet Field. Canst not add thereto the name of my master? I have somewhat in my pouch that I saved in my good lord's service, nor can I better bestow it than to this end." 'Twas a strange thing, doubtless, to ask of a priest, but the man spake according to his light, and I loved him for his faithfulness. "Nay," said I, when he would have given me some gold pieces that he carried in a bag; "nay, it would ill become me to take pay for such service, both from my lord the King and from another. Keep thy pieces; or, if thou wilt, bestow them upon the poor, for almsdeeds go up even as do prayers for an offering of a sweet savour to God. But I will not forget thy master, nor do I think that I transgress against either charity or duty, if I make mention of his name, if not upon my lips, at least within my heart." Then the man departed, but somewhat downcast, as it seemed to me, thinking haply, that that which had cost him nothing would nothing avail.

I have been considering much with myself from the day that I first heard of this office how, my due service being finished—and this is indeed but a small matter—I had best bestow my time. I know that chantry priests are often but lightly spoken of, being, 'tis said, men of a mean spirit who, that they may live in idleness, are content with small wage, which, nevertheless, they do eke out in no reputable fashion. But that any man must of necessity be idle I do not allow, so long as there are the unlearned to be taught and the sick and afflicted to be comforted. And now I will set down my resolves.

First, then, I purpose to teach the rudiments of learning to such lads as their fathers, being of yeoman's degree or the like, shall be willing to send to me. It seemeth to me a shameful thing that in this realm of England there should be so slender a provision for the teaching of the young. Schools there are at Oxford, and at Cambridge, and at Winchester, and at Eton, and in some of the monasteries, but not in all (though how should a monk's time be better bestowed than on such works), but 'tis but a small portion at the best of our English youth that are taught even so much as to read and to write. Of the poor wretches that are brought to the gallows, of whom there are I know not how many thousands in the year, how few do claim what men of the law call the "benefit of clergy," that is, that a man shall not die if he can read and write. For myself I cannot discern why all men, though they be but churls, so that they have but the necessary reason, should not be so taught. But this, I doubt not, is a fancy that is never like to become fact in this world. Yet will I do my little part in this great work, and so make a return not of thanks only, but of service for the great benefits which by the grace of God and the favour of good Bishop William I myself received.

This I can not do till I dwell in my own house, which I hear will scarce be finished for a year to come. Meanwhile I will make such preparation as I may. Haply I may get some help in the way of books from the school-master of St. Albans; and some I can buy, having more of money than I can spend on myself. And I doubt not that in London such things may be more readily bought than elsewhere.

Also I shall doubtless find some sick folk to whom, with leave first had of the parsons of Barnet and Hadley, I may minister.

Nor shall I want for due recreation. An I cared for hunting and fowling, such sport I might have in plenty, for there is a great abundance of hares and conies and of birds of all kinds; but this pursuit I shall not follow, having no inclination thereto, not to speak of the ill-repute in which hunting priests are commonly held. But angling, which by common consent is allowed to spiritual men (though indeed the difference is of word rather than deed), I shall practice with moderation. Rivers there are none at hand, and of streams but few and these small, but ponds and lakes are plenty. Finally, I have a good hope that I may yet pracise something of my art. If indeed I seek to read a book for any space of time beyond the shortest then there cometh upon me the old trouble of the head, but I have made pictures in colours without damage, so far as I could tell to myself. And here I shall have a great store of things which I may so copy. I do not fear but what I shall have abundance wherewith to occupy my time. Finally, the place, I like right-well. The air, may be, is somewhat over keen for them that have ailments of the chest, but 'tis marvellously pure and fresh. And the people are a simple, kindly folk, among whom I shall be well content to live. I could wish indeed that there were not so many masterful vagabonds on the road. These are found to be coming, as it were, in a perpetual stream to London, which indeed draweth to itself both bad and good, as a magnet draweth the iron. The number of such is now greatly increased by the late wars, and will be diminished, I have a good hope, when the times shall be more settled. As for myself I fear them but little; for though they, for the most part, would as lief rob a priest as a common man, yet I have the greater security of poverty. Though my abode be lonely, and indeed it is not within hearing of any house, small or great, yet I shall dwell safely.

I doubt much whether I shall ever have occasion again to write again in this book, for what can happen to a poor chantry priest that shall be worthy note? Yet will I keep it by me, ready to be used, if haply such occasion should arise.

OF THOMAS CAXTON AND OTHERS

The First day of September, 1477.

I HAVE this day returned from London, where I have seen a sight so notable that I am constrained to make some mention of it. There is a most worthy and learned gentleman of this country, John Goodere, of the parish of Hadley, who is a great lover of books, a quality not common in these parts, or indeed in any other of which I have knowledge. This Master Goodere cometh to me some ten days since or thereabouts and biddeth me to dinner on the morrow. Saith he, "An thou wilt come, thou shalt not only see a certain friend of thine, but also hear of a most wonderful invention." So on the morrow I go, and so soon as I come into Master Goodere's parlour, I find besides mine host and Mistress Alice, his wife, and his son John, a lad of some sixteen years, to whom in time past I taught the rudiments, one of the brotherhood of St. Albans, John Herford by name, who came into the house near about the time of my own entering, and with whom I had had no small friendship. He was in his degree a lover of learning and books, and but a short while before my departing from the house had been appointed to be schoolmaster. After dinner, of which it will suffice to write that it was a well-furnished entertainment, saith Master Goodere, "Thou hast sojourned, methinks, Sir Thomas, in this neighbourhood for a matter of six years or thereabouts?"

"'Tis even so," I answered. "I came hither—that is to say, to Barnet town—on the eve of St. Peter in the year of the battle; nor have I travelled abroad for so much as a day."

"Then," said he, "I propose that thou shalt have thy will, if will it be, to-morrow, coming with me and Sir John Herford here to London, where thou shalt see such a sight as thou hast never looked upon in thy life. What it is, I will not tell thee; but thou hast the word of a gentleman that it will be worth thy pains, ay, even were they ten times so great as they shall be.

And if thou confess not as much when thou hast seen, then will I forfeit one hundred pounds, or what would be more to thy liking than money, all the books that I have."

"But who," say I, "shall sing my mass—for I take it that we shall scarce go and return in one day? "

"That," said Brother John, "is a matter of which we have been not unmindful. For know that this is no new plot which we have laid against thee. See this letter from my lord Abbot of Westminster, in which he giveth licence for Sir Thomas Aylmer to say mass in one of his chapels at Westminster for as many days as it shall please him so to do."

Then said Master Goodere, "Thou shalt dine with me to-morrow, Sir Thomas, if thou wilt; and, as we have a journey to make, the dinner shall not be later than half-past eleven in the forenoon. So will we set forth at one of the clock or there about, and be in London before sunset."

To this I agreed, and after had much talk with my host, and also with Brother Herford, about matters in the Abbey, where since my departing many things have been changed, the late Prior, Walling of Wallingford, having been chosen to be Abbot, and Thomas Nayland, that was before master of the kitchen, to be Prior, On the morrow we journeyed to London without mishap on our way, and lay that night at the house of William Pratt, in the parish of St. Margaret, Westminster, a citizen and mercer, and, as I should judge from the plenishing of his house, a man of much substance. On the morrow I said mass in the chapel of St. Edmund, where, indeed, Sir Humphrey Bourchier lies buried. And about nine of the clock in the forenoon Master Pratt leadeth us to a tenement in the Almonry, which standeth on the outside of the Abbey. This tenement was a building of wood, some sixty feet, as I should judge, in length and about half as much in breadth. 'Twas divided into three chambers, into the greatest of which we entered at our coming. And that I may declare at once what we saw therein, 'twas the art and mystery of Printing. There were some six men in the chamber, standing at their work without their doublets, like to those that have some great toil, as of reaping or the like, upon their hands. Of these every one had his several place as near as might be to the windows for the better advantage of the light, which indeed was somewhat scanty, and doth oft times fail altogether by reason of the mists from the river and the smoke of many fires from the town. And before each was a great box, and in it many parts, and in each part a multitude of pieces of lead, or of some other substance (but of what it was I took no special note). Handling one of these pieces I perceived that it was of an inch's length or thereabouts, and that at the end thereof was the similitude of a letter, or, may be, of two letters. These the man would take one by one, as he had need of them, from the parts of the box wherein they severally lay, and would set them side by side in a line, from the left hand to the right. And when he had ended one line he set another below it, and yet another, some twenty or thirty altogether, till he had made, as it were, a page. And all these were made fast so that they could not shift from their place.

This being done the page was set in a box, and the man took in his hand what they called in the place a ball ('twas of wood with leather upon it, and under the leather wool). This ball he dipped in a pan of ink that stood by, and inked the page therewith, all over, as evenly as he might. This being done he took in his hand a portion of paper, larger by somewhat than the page, so that there might be a space remaining above and below and on either side. This paper he made fast to a board, and the board he pressed upon the page, lightly indeed, yet so that there was not any place which it did not touch. And when he had taken the paper away it had the writing, or, I should rather say, the printing of the letters, upon it, plain to see. Then he laid upon the page another and yet another portion of paper. And if he saw that the letters grew faint, he would add more ink with the ball. And this he did till he had made as many copies as he would; and indeed I was told that of the book which was then in hand they were minded to make a thousand copies.

That this printing was as shapely and fair to see as the writing of a ready scribe I say not. Nay, there were many blemishes in it, for certain of the letters were faint where the ink was somewhat scanty, and others were over-dark where it had too much abounded; and I noted two or three places where the man had set one letter wrongly in the place of another. But that it was fairer to behold, and such as a man might more easily read, than the writing which is commonly to be seen, I doubt not. Nor is it to be doubted that such faults as it hath will be mended by the ingenuity of them that practice the craft, even as the art of writing hath now come to such perfection as it never had before. But the marvel of it is, that in the space of a day a man may make with these 'types'—for so they call the letters wherewith the printing is done—more than another may accomplish with his pen in his whole life.

After this I passed into the smaller chamber, where sat two men binding the sheets together. But this part of the work I knew already, for it differed not from the binding of books that are written, save only that it was done with less care and regard for show. Nevertheless, I did not conceive within my own mind how great a change this said art of printing shall work till I saw how great a heap of paper there was before each of the binders.

When we were entered again into the greater chamber there stood there, talking with one of them that set the types in order, a man of fair presence, having, as I should judge, five and fifty years of age or thereabouts. Then saith Master Pratt, "'Tis the master himself," and he led us to him. The other of the company were already known to him; and when he had greeted these, saith Master Pratt to me, "This is Master Caxton, sometime citizen and mercer of London, and now printer of Westminster." And to Master Caxton, "This is Sir Thomas Aylmer, now chantry priest of Barnet, sometime monk of St. Alban's Abbey, and a notable scribe, as I have understood. So now I have brought the new and the old together."

Master Caxton stretched forth his hand to me and saith, "Doubt not that we shall agree together as the Old Testament and the New agree together, if I may compare small things to great. But now—for these things, I take it, are new to thee, but these thy friends have seen them before—I will show thee this place and the mysteries of my craft."

Then he showed me all the work, making clear to me sundry things that I had not understood before; and when I had seen everything he took me into his own house, and gave me a book, and "This," he said, "is the first book that ever was printed in this realm of England; but in Flanders and elsewhere books have been printed for some years past."

(This book beareth the title, "Dictes and Sayings of the Philosophers," and is done into English from the French by my lord Rivers, brother to the Queen. In his Prologue my lord saith, that being on a journey to the shrine of St. James of Campostella he fell in with a very valiant knight of Saxony, Sir Lewis de Bretaylles, who showed him this book writ in French, and that being much edified therewith, he hath rendered it into English. To this Master Caxton hath added a Prologue writ by his own pen, "Touching Women.")

Then Master Caxton set forth to me how he had come to learn this art of printing. "When I ceased," said he, "to be governor of the English merchants at Bruges—

about which occupation, as it hath nought to do with this present subject, I will not speak—I took service with my lady Margaret, Duchess of Burgundy, that is sister to the King. This I did because I was wearied and worn with the cares of trade, and desired to have more leisure for letters and books, things that I have loved from my youth up. But lest I should fall into sloth and idleness, to which some men give themselves over under cover of book learning, I set myself to render certain works from other tongues into English, my good lady the Duchess approving and encouraging me therein. Among them was 'The Relation of the Histories of Troy,' rendered into French from the Latin by Raoul le Fevre, that was chaplain to Philip de Good, sometime Duke of Burgundy. This I did into English, and when I had presented it to my lady the Duchess, and many that I knew in the city desired to have it for themselves, I learned from a certain Master Collard, that is a printer at Bruges, this art and craft, for I found that it was an intolerable weariness to make as many copies as were desired. Verily it was a marvellous thing to me, as I doubt not it hath been to thee, to see so many copies finished in the space of one day. And after, I having a great desire to return to my own country, and having good hopes of favour from my lord the King, and believing also that I had in this same printing as honest a trade and as profitable withal, as a man can follow, I left service with my lady the Duchess, and having purchased the necessary implements of the craft, came with them to this place, where I have hired of the Abbey of Westminster. And this book, which I do desire thee to keep for a remembrance of me, is the first that hath ever been printed in this kingdom of England. It may ill compare with the masterpieces of thy handicraft—and indeed it were passing strange if this art which hath lived but twenty years at the most should match with that which hath been now growing for so many generations—yet it hath in it, I do believe, such a promise as I can neither express with my tongue nor conceive in my heart. Verily, Sir Priest, I do almost tremble to think what this same art of printing shall grow to in times to come. Then shall knowledge be no more the inheritance of a few, but the possession of the many, so that there shall be in the poor man's cottage more books than be now found in the noble's hall. And when these things are so what shall not happen? Thinkest thou that men will be content to take from others that which they can find out for themselves? Many things will be changed, I doubt not. I pray God that it may be for the bettering both of Church and State."

After this, Master Caxton entertained us in sumptuous fashion, as is the wont of the citizens, and we departed, Master Herford talking much of what he had seen.

Sept. 1, 1480.

'Tis three years since I last wrote in this book, and I have heard this day something that calls to my mind the substance of my last writing. Nothing would content Brother Herford but he must set up in the Abbey such a printing press as he had seen at Master Caxton's. And this he did, but not without much opposing from certain of the brotherhood. There were those who love to stand upon the old ways, and like not what they call new-fangled things. Others there were who feared from their heart what this new thing should grow to, and they that worked in the *scriptorium*, and were highly esteemed for their skill of penmanship, were ill-disposed to that which seemed like to destroy their craft. So it was that there were many who hindered. Nevertheless, Master Herford was not discouraged, and having gained the ear of the Abbot, who looked upon things somewhat more broadly than do others of the brethren, he had his way. And I have this day received the first fruits of his skill, to wit, "The New Rhetoric of Brother Lawrence William of Saone." I do greatly rejoice in this thing, for I am persuaded in my mind that ill will befall the Abbeys and Priories of this realm, being, as they are, so wealthy, if they are not foremost in every good that is done.

October 4, 1486.

There is ill news come from St. Albans. Master Herford, sometime schoolmaster, and late printer, of whom I have before written in this book, is dead, and the business of printing in that place is ended. He had during the space of six years finished many excellent books, of which the most notable was "The St. Alban's Chronicle;" but there were now, as I have said, many against him; and as it seemeth to me, when there was a change in the government of the house (for John of Wallingford died in the year 1484, and Thomas Ramryge was chosen in his room) these prevailed. This I speak not of my own knowledge, but there are rumours to this effect. Certain it is that the printing is stopped, and Master Herford is dead. But whether he died of vexation and disappointment, as some report, or in the course of nature, I do not venture to affirm. But I do lament from my heart that which hath been done. There will be none willing to write in the *scriptorium*, knowing that their labor can be so easily surpassed by this art of printing. And if there be no *scriptorium,* how shall the brethren be employed? And if they be not employed, seeing the idleness is the mother of many evils, how shall they be hindered from falling into bad ways? The houses which follow the order of St. Benedict do not in all things maintain such strictness of rule as may be found elsewhere, as, for example, to wit, in the houses of the Carthusians. But they have ever loved letters and learning. And if these be taken from them—and verily there are at this moment of writing scarce any that do care for them—what shall be the end?

OF THE BATTLE OF FLODDEN

The 1st day of October, 1513.

MORE than thirty years have passed (a whole generation as generations are reckoned in the life of man) since last I wrote in this book. And indeed I never thought to have opened it again. For my life in this place hath been altogether without anything that was noteworthy. Many great and notable things have indeed come to pass in the world without—one king murdered, another slain in battle, another dying in his bed, so that now there sitteth upon this throne of England the fourth in order from my lord King Edward; moreover, there hath been one making claim to the kingdom of whom men doubt to this day whether he were a true prince or a false pretender. Also a new world hath been found beyond the sea, and of the old world many regions that before were not known have been visited. In Europe have happened many things strange and terrible. The infidels have gathered strength so that they have seemed like to overthrow Christendom, which nevertheless hath been in yet greater peril from its own divisions, notably in having for its Chief one whom, for his wickedness, no secular State would have endured. But these things have passed me, and I heard of them only by report. But I have passed my days in the discharging of my office, and in teaching of the young (of which work, indeed, I have ever had as much as I had strength to perform) and in ministering to the sick. Also—for time in some things hath added to my strength rather than taken from it—I have given no little time to study, and especially to the perfecting of myself in the Greek tongue, which, of late years especially, since the coming of a certain Erasmus, a Hollander, to this realm, hath been much followed

But now, being an old man of more than three-score years and ten, I take up this book again, purposing to write in it of certain things which concern my former life.

Yestereven about five of the clock there came running to me a lad, son to my host of the White Horse Inn in Barnet, with a message from his father praying that I would come with such speed as I might, for that a young man that was like to die earnestly desired to see a priest, and that the parson of Barnet chanced to be abroad. So I went, and found the young man lying upon a bed in a chamber of the inn, very grievously hurt by the falling of his horse. My host told me that he was one of the following of the Lord Admiral, and saith he, "See, Sir Thomas, how strange are the chances of this mortal life. This young man hath been with my lord Howard, the Admiral, in many perils of storm and battle, standing, as I am told, by his side when Andrew Barton, the pirate of Scotland, was slain; and even now he is returning from a most fierce battle that bath been fought between the King's men and King James of Scotland, through which battle he went without so much as a scratch upon him; and lo! now, when he is but a few miles from his journey's end, his horse putteth his foot into a hole which some boys have made for their silly sport, and casteth him headlong to the ground so that he is like to die."

When I had done my priest's duty to him, and had spoken some few words of comfort such as he could bear, for he was very weak, I turned to depart, promising—for he was loath to let me go, poor lad!—that I would return on the morrow, I was aware of a man standing by the chamber door, that seemed to be one in authority. He had, I should judge, about forty-and-five years of age, and was tall of stature, three inches or so more than six feet, and of a comely face, though much embrowned with the sun. And when I saw him, I seemed to be aware of somewhat in his countenance that I had seen before; but what it was I knew not. And as I looked upon him, wondering in my mind what this might be, with something, haply, of the look of one that is distraught (for indeed I was strangely moved), he smiled, but in a courteous fashion, and, bowing his head, said, "Thy blessing, if thou wilt, father." And when he spake his voice was as his face, something that I knew and yet knew not. Then I gave him my blessing, thinking little,

I fear me, of the words I spake, but searching my heart for some remembrance of what I had seen and heard. And then there seemed to come before me, as with a sudden flash, the face of Joan Eliot, as I had seen her for the last time some fifty years before. So I said, "Tell me, sir, is thy name Norton?" And he, astonished, for it was now his turn to marvel, answered, "Yea, it is." "And thy mother's name Joan, that was by birth Eliot, and thy father's Edward Norton?" And he, marvelling yet more and more, made answer, "'Tis as thou sayest, but how hast thou such knowledge of my kindred?" "That," said I, "I cannot declare in this company. But come and see me at my house, and we will talk together." "That will I right willingly; and, indeed I cannot depart till I have seen how it will go with this poor lad. Look for me, then, if it please thee, in an hour's time, when I shall set matters in order for our sojourn here this night."

So about eight of the clock he came to me. And first I told how, many years before, I had known his mother, who was not then wedded, and had had also some brief acquaintance with his father, and that I was greatly desirous to hear how they had fared.

Then he said, "My father departed this life eight years ago come the seventeenth day of this month, being nigh upon fourscore years of age. He took service after his marriage with the Earl of March, that was afterwards King Edward the Fourth, and did him good service in divers place, following him when he fled beyond the sea, being driven from his kingdom by the Earl of Warwick, and was present also at Barnet Field. So the King gave him a place of profit about the Court. But when King Richard reigned in his brother's room, my father, being in peril of his life (for the King knew that he was in special favour with the Duke of Buckingham), fled over the sea to the Earl of Richmond, that was afterwards King, who, when he was established upon his throne, restored to him his place. And when he died the King continued a pension out of the profits of the same to my mother, which she receiveth to this day."

"And where doth thy mother live?" said I.

"In London," he answered, "or, I should rather say in Westminster, in her own house which my father bought twenty years or so before that he died."

"And how fareth she for health?"

"Somewhat poorly; for she was taken with a quartan-ague in the year of my father's death, and what with this and with her grief, for they had lived together in all love and honour for forty-and-two years, she was like to have died. And now she is very feeble; and indeed she hath more than three score and ten years of age."

"And thy uncle, John Eliot, cloth he yet live?"

"Yea, in great repute and honour on his lands in Shropshire. He was minded in his youth, I have heard him say, to follow some learned profession, and for that end proceeded to his degrees at Oxford. But when the time came his father died, and his brother also, being taken both of them with the plague, that was very grievous in those parts, so that he was constrained to follow a farmer's life, lest his mother should be left destitute. Nor did he miss his reward. For in a short space after there came to him no small wealth by the will of a certain kinsman of his mother. Therewith he bought certain lands that bordered on his own, and hath now a fair estate of three hundred pounds by the year, and is a justice of the peace, and a man of no small weight and authority."

"And now," said I, "tell me about thyself. Hast any brother or sister?"

"Nay, I am an only one. But if thou wouldst hear my story, thou shalt have it in brief. Nothing would content me when I grew to proper age but I must take service as a soldier. And my desire had indeed as speedy fulfilment as I could wish. For when my father fled, as I have said, to King Henry, I went with him; and when the King came to England I was in his company (but my father tarried abroad, being taken with a sudden sickness, that was indeed not unwelcome, for that it hindered him from encountering his friends that had been in battle). So I came to be at Bosworth Field, being then seventeen years of age. Afterwards I went with Sir Edward Poynings into Flanders, and with the Earl of Surrey into Scotland (what time the King of Scotland did harbour Perkin Warbeck), and in divers other expeditions of which there is no need to speak. And two years since, being used, as is the custom of many in these times, to serve indifferently by land and sea, I followed Sir Thomas Howard, brother to the Lord Admiral. Now the King had heard that one Andrew Barton, a Scottish man, saying that the King of Scotland had war with the Portugals, robbed every nation. And when he took Englishmen's goods, he affirmed that they were Portugal goods, and thus he robbed at every haven's mouth. So the King sent the Admiral and his brother Sir Thomas in all haste to the sea; who made ready two ships with all speed. These two by chance of weather were severed. And Sir Thomas, lying in the Downs, for the winds were contrary, saw the said Andrew making towards Scotland, and chased him so fast that he overtook him, and there was a sore battle between them. Andrew now blew his whistle to encourage his men, but Sir Thomas Howard and the Englishmen did so valiantly that by clean strength they entered the main deck. The Scots fought sore on the hatches, but in conclusion Andrew was taken, being so sorely wounded that he died. And with him was taken his ship the Lion. This lad that is lying sick yonder bare himself right bravely in this battle, than which, I give thee my word as a Christian, I never saw fiercer. Verily these Scots are doughty adversaries, as I have but just now had good reason to know, being just returned from Flodden."

"Tell me," said I, "somewhat about this battle, of which we men of peace have heard some rumours, indeed, but nothing certain."

"I came with Sir Thomas Howard, being the Lord Admiral, on Sunday the fourth day of September, having made all haste from the sea so soon as we heard of the gathering of the Scots; and there were one thousand men of us that had served with my lord for two years and more. There we found my lord Surrey. But the King of Scotland was encamped on a hill called Flodden. And this place was very strong, being defended on the right hand with a river called Till, that was so strong and deep that it could not conveniently be crossed. And on the back part there were such craggy rocks and thick woods that it was impossible to assail it to any advantage. And on the forepart, where it could be easily approached, the King had set all his ordnance by great trenches, which he had caused to be dug.

"Then the Earl sendeth a herald to the King saying that he had done ill to ravage the country of his brother the King of England without reason, and provoking him to try the justice of his cause in battle by the Friday next ensuing. And this the King of the Scots promised that he would do. Nevertheless, though he had a great desire to fight, by the advice of his lords he removed not from his place. Thereupon the Earl of Surrey, because the place wherein he was lodged was full of mire and marshes, and because his men were almost famished for lack of sufficient victuals, determined to use all ways to constrain the Scottish king to come down from his hill. To this end he raised his camp, passing over the river Till to a more commodious ground by the Barmore wood.

"And now the two camps lay with the Till between them; and because the one was within a culverin-shot of the other, they ceased not to bestow powder and shot, the one at the other, but without doing any great hurt.

"After this Sir Thomas Howard, having seen all the country from the top of a hill in those parts, declared to the Earl that if he would again move his army, and pass the water of Till a little above, and by fetching a small compass show himself at the back of his enemies, the King of the Scots would either be enforced to give battle, or would be stopped from, receiving victuals out of Scotland. This the Earl did, and when the King saw it he also raised his camp, and made haste to take a certain hill which he feared lest the English should take before him. And this he did, for the smoke from the burning of the cabins where the Scots had lodged was so great that the English, though being within one mile of him, knew not that he had raised his camp. But when the Earl of Surrey came to the foot of the said hill, and seeing the King at the top perceived that it was not steep or hard to ascend, he determined to fight with the Scottish host before they should have leisure to fortify their camp.

"Herewith calling together his people, he made unto them a brief oration, showing them what necessity they had to show their manhood and what just causes to fight against their enemies. This done, the Englishmen demanded to be led forthwith to battle. From this Lord Surrey had good hope of victory.

"His army he divided into four, giving the vanguard to the Lord Admiral, and the rearward to Sir Edward Stanley. The middle ward he led himself; and the Lord Dacres with a number of horsemen was set apart by himself to succour where need should seem to appear.

"The King of Scots, on the other hand, thought that he had us at an advantage, both of place and of numbers. He also divided his host into three, standing himself in the middle.

"When we marched up the hill the Scots' cannon opened fiercely upon us, but did small damage, shooting over our heads. And when we encountered them first, Sir

Thomas Howard, having one wing of the vanguard, was beaten down, and would have been slain but for the Bastard of Heron. After, the Lord Dacres coming with his horsemen relieved him, and the rest of the van pressing on drave back the Scots on the right wing. On the left wing, Sir Edward Stanley with his archers so troubled the Scots with a storm of arrows, that they brake up their close array, and fought separated one from the other. Sir Edward Stanley perceiving this brought up three bands which he had kept in store for this purpose, and fell upon the open side of the enemy, who, after much stout fighting, turned their backs.

"Meanwhile the King had joined battle with the Earl of Surrey. And though he saw that his wings had been sorely handled, he abated not his courage, but fell upon our people with much fury. The archers could not stay him and his following, so well armed were they; but they brake through the Earl's battle and well-nigh overthrew his standards. The King himself, being on foot, for he and his nobles had sent away their horses at the beginning, fought right valiantly, as also on our side did my lord Surrey. But when the victory was uncertain, up cometh first Sir Edward Stanley, and after him the Lord Dacres with his horsemen, upon the backs of the Scots. Then these, being assaulted on all sides, were constrained to fight in a round compass. And after a while the King, seeing his standard-bearer stricken down at his side, rushed forth into the thickest press and was there slain. With him were slain also the Archbishop of St. Andrews, and two bishops and four abbots—for the spiritual persons among the Scots do fight as sturdily as do the lay. How many more perished on either side I know not, having departed from the field before a reckoning was made. For by desire of the Earl I made my course straight to London, and have sent some three or four of my company that were best horsed, bearing letters from the Earl to the King, and also, as a pledge and token of victory, the King of Scots' gauntlet."

Edward Norton tarried in Barnet for three days, during which time I had much talk with him. And on the fourth day, the young man having beyond all expectation revived, he departed, not without promise, both on his part and on mine, that we should meet again.

OF MISTRESS JOAN

The 12th day of October, 1513.

I AM newly returned from London, whither indeed I had scarce thought to have gone again. But seven days after the departing of Edward Norton (of which I have written above), I felt, as it were, a drawing of the spirit which did not suffer me to rest. At the first I knew not what this might mean, and doubted whether it might not be some sickness growing upon me; but in a short space it became manifest to me, even as though it had been writ before my very eyes, that Joan Norton desired to see me. How this came to pass I know not, but God knoweth that it is true. For though I have thought daily of Joan Eliot for fifty-and-two years, and have made mention of her in my prayers, it hath never come into my mind that I should see her, for it seemed to me that it was ordered otherwise for her and me. Knowing therefore that Master Francis Goodere (grandson to that John Goodere of whom I have written before) was wont to go to London about this time, having moneys to receive, I went to him, and found him about to set forth in his coach, for he had his wife with him. So I journeyed in their company to London, and thence took boat to Westminster. And when the wherry came near to the landing-place I saw Edward Norton stand by the waterside, who, when he had given me his hand to help me to the shore, said, "Verily she seemeth to have the gift of prophecy. For she said to me but half-an-hour ago, 'Go, Edward, to the river stairs and bring him hither;' and though I was loath to leave her, I went. And indeed yesterday she knew beforehand of the coming of my Uncle John, her brother, whereof we had had no warning." So we went together to the house, which lies on the north side of the church-yard of St. Margaret; having entered into which I found in a parlour the friend of my youth, John Eliot. He sat in a chair by the fireside, overcome with sleep, for he had journeyed almost without halt from his home. At our coming in he roused himself and stood up; but whether because he was but newly waked from his slumber, or because of my monk's habit, or because he thought not to see me, knew me not, but said, "Thy blessing, sir." But when I had given it and added also, "Thou hast it, John, with all my heart," then he remembered me.

Then he told me that the leech had said that his sister could scarce live out the day, and that the priest of St. Margaret's had been with her in the morning. And "now," he said, "she sleepeth. But the woman that tendeth her will advise us of her waking."

I shall not seek to set down in this place how we talked together, for we had, so to say, a whole life of which to speak one to the other. As for my story, it hath been told already in this book; and his was but brief as the story of one that hath lived in prosperity and happiness is like to be. Yet that we lacked not matter need scarce be said, opening each his heart to other, so that we took no count of the passing of time. It was near upon midnight when the woman coming down from the chamber told us that Mistress Norton waked. Thereupon we went up; and I, when first I saw her, deemed that she was dead already, for her eyes were shut, and there was such peace upon her face as could never, it seemed, be broken any more. But when we came near to her bedside, she opened her eyes and smiled upon us, looking first to him and then to me. And when she had spoken for a brief space to him—but what she said I know not, for her voice was exceeding low (nor indeed did I seek to hear)—she turned her face to me, and said, "I have been happy; and thou, Brother Thomas?" "God hath given me peace," I answered. Then she whispered that her son should come up. So he came, and when he had knelt down by her side she laid her right hand upon his head and blessed him. After this she reached forth her right hand to her brother and to me her left, and so remained for the space of about half an hour, speaking nothing. Then she said, "He shall make all things new," and so passed away; but of the time of her passing we knew not, so peaceful was it and without pain.

MY LAST WRITING IN THIS BOOK

The 1st day of May, 1516.

AS I draw near to the end of my life—and indeed my years have already approached that which the Psalmist hath laid down as the further limit of the days of man—some things that were before dark to me become clear, and some that I thought much to be desired appear no longer to be wished; and some for which I had scarce dared to hope, or of which I had not so much as thought, have come to pass beyond all expectation.

It is now more than fifty years since, being entertained at the Priory of Worcester and seeing how the brethren dwelt in great peace and content, I conceived the desire of being a monk. And though when this desire was fulfilled I found the life to fall somewhat short of my hope, yet it was no small trouble to me when I was constrained to leave it for another. But now the matter is otherwise with me, so that I rather am thankful that I have been led away from that very place wherein I most desired to stay. And this thankfulness I first felt some twenty-and-five years since when, by the commandment of the Holy Father himself, Pope Innocent VIII. Dr. Morton, being then Archbishop of Canterbury, made a visitation of the House of St. Alban, of which visitation I wrote nothing at the time in this book, being neither willing to believe nor able to deny the things which the said archbishop laid to the charge of them that aforetime were my brethren, but of which I will now set down so much, to wit: that some things were magnified beyond the truth to the end that the King, who looked rather to the increasing of his treasure than to the encouragement of good living, might with the more reason exact a fine from the wrong-doers, but that the truth itself was such as no Christian man could hear without shame; that there had been much sinful and riotous living and very grievous breaking of vows; and that there had been wasting of the revenues of the house; cutting down of timber beyond custom, so that whole woods had vanished away and selling of jewels and cups, nay of the very offerings from the shrine of St. Alban himself. And I do hear from those that are not like to speak falsely in such matters, that though there be houses in which all things are done decently and in order, yet there are others, and these especially of the smaller sort, in which such like abuses do flourish to this very day. Moreover I can see for myself—for I do hear it not unfrequently in the common talk of men—that this realm of England is growing somewhat weary of monks and their ways, and this the more now that their chief office of promoting learning and letters hath passed, it would seem, into other hands. And of this I heard but just now a most notable confirmation. For being at the house of the Worshipful Sir John More, of whom I will write more presently, the talk fell upon my lord of Winchester, than whom there is not in this realm of England a more notable scholar and patron of learning. The said Bishop was minded to found a college for a warden and certain monks and scholars that should belong to the Priory of St. Swithin in Winchester; and indeed had already begun to build the same when he chanced to talk with my lord Bishop of Exeter on the matter. Whereupon saith my lord of Exeter, "Nay, my lord, shall we build houses and provide livelihoods for a swarm of buzzing monks, who have already more than they are like to hold, and whose end and fall we ourselves may live to see?" Whereupon the said Bishop hath changed his counsel, and will set up another college at Oxford, whereof much, I hear, is already finished, so that it shall in all likelihood be opened this same year.

And now to speak of a certain thing of which I have thought many times since the days of my youth, and which I have now in my old age been suffered by the grace of God to see with mine eyes.

This Sir John More, of whom I have written above, hath a house of which the name is Gobions, or, as some of the country-folk call it, More Place (for it hath been the inheritance of the Mores for sundry generations). He is an old man, having indeed been born in the same year with myself, and hath been for many years one of the King's judges. I have had acquaintance with him for these many years, the said acquaintance beginning, if my memory serveth me, in the year 1489, and on this occasion. In this year the plague was in London, and Sir John dwelt longer than was his common use at his house of Gobions, to which he for the most part resorted only after that the courts had risen. Now he had a son, Thomas by name, that had then eleven years of age, and was a scholar in a school of some note in London, to wit, St. Antony's in Threadneedle Street, where he had made notable progress in learning. It disturbed him much that his son should endure such interruption to his studies, the lad himself being, I do verily believe, not the less vexed thereat. Seeking thus for some one who should give the boy instruction, that the time might not be altogether wasted, there was brought him a report of me, who did then teach the rudiments of polite learning to such as were willing to learn, and indeed continued so to do so long as my strength permitted. So for the space of three months or thereabouts the lad came daily to me, riding on a little horse which his father had given him, and would not be hindered by any rain, howsoever great; and if his mother, being careful of his health, after the manner of women, was like to hinder him for cause of the weather, he would escape out of the house by stealth. He had marvellous parts, such as I never saw in any other whom I taught, and for jests there was no one that could match him. Nor did I give him such instruction that year only, but also afterwards, till indeed he had passed beyond my poor powers of teaching. This Thomas More has risen to a high place in the state, and is like to rise to yet higher. For when he was but twenty-four years of age he was a burgess of the Commons' House, in which place he showed a notable freedom, not altogether to the liking of them that were in power. And of late years he has been in high repute as an advocate, in which profession he has had such returns of money for his labours as have scarce been known before in this country, that is to say, more than three hundred and fifty pounds by the year. And even now he hath been sent by the King's Majesty on an embassage to Flanders, from which office he hath returned with much credit and success. But for all his honours, to me he hath shown not kindness only but reverence, forgetting not that I taught him in old time, and ordering himself to me as doth a scholar to his master.

Some days ago being called to dinner at Sir John More's house (whither I was conveyed in a carriage, as his custom with me is), I found, besides two or three others, gentlemen of these parts, or whom Francis Goodere was one, Master Thomas More, and with him a right worthy and learned divine of whom I have heard many speak, and that with much praise, for these twenty years past, yet have never chanced to see; that is to say, Master Colet, the Dean of St. Paul's Church in London. There be some, I know, that fear him, thinking that he goeth overmuch after novelties and forsaketh the soundness of the faith. And indeed I have heard that my lord of London would gladly have deposed him from his dignity, yea, and have brought him into judgment for heresy, but that the King's Majesty bare him harmless. 'Tis certain that he is a lover of the new learning, for the better promoting of which he hath newly founded a grammar school in London; and he hath so far departed from the old way, that he hath studied the Greek tongue; yea, and did lecture at Oxford on the Epistles of St. Paul, as so written. (Methinks that they who do rail at Greek forget in marvellous fashion that the words of Christ and His Apostles are written down for our edification in that tongue.) I noted that he gave me but a passing regard, as though it were enough to have seen my monk's habit (for he is no lover of monks). Then saith Master Thomas More, "I would have you acquainted, Master Dean, with Sir Thomas Aylmer, chantry priest of Barnet," which he did of mischief, knowing that Master Colet, if he loveth monks but little, loveth chantry priests yet less. Then when he had greeted me—not discourteously indeed, for this it is not in the nature of the man to do, but as one that seeketh not further acquaintance proceedeth Master More, "and is learned also in the Greek tongue;" at which I saw Master Dean regard me with no little amazement. But before he could speak Master More saith further, "I do hope that my father will not turn him from his house as one that hath about him a dangerous commodity. Say, father, didst thou not cut short my sojourn in Oxford, fearing that I should learn overmuch Greek, and so fall into dangerous heresies?" Then the old man laughed and said, "'Twas even so; but I am wiser now, having grown to years of discretion, for then I was but a youth of three-score or so." After this Master Colet and I had much talk together, and I told him how I had gained some knowledge of the Greek tongue, with which relation he was mightily pleased. And he would have me sit by him at dinner, desiring, it would seem, to make amends if perchance I had thought him wanting in courtesy.

After dinner Master Thomas discoursed in wittier fashion than ever before I heard from the lips of man on a certain book which he hath it in his mind to write. 'Tis of the ensample of a State, and he will call it by the title of Utopia, which may be interpreted "Nowhere." I cannot call to mind a tenth part of the things that he told us, but I do remember that he said that these said Utopians have it for a fixed rule that they will make no treaties with other nations, as having learnt that there is nothing in this world that can so easily be broken; and that those who rule this commonwealth have ordered it in such wise as never commonwealth was ordered upon earth, for every man's house has a fair garden to it, and their watercourses such that none lack of clean water as much as they need; and that there are hospitals where all sick folk may be healed, none being in danger of infection from another, and common halls where the citizens make good cheer together with all sobriety; and that every child, from the highest to the lowest, is taught even as though he were to follow the calling of a lawyer or a priest.

When he had finished his discourse he opened the door of the chamber and rang upon a bell that was hard by. Thereupon came a serving-man carrying something wrapped in a cover of black silk. This Master Thomas More taking in his hand gave to the Dean, saying, "There is no man in this realm of England that deserveth better to have the first handling of this treasure than thou. Take it, then, as my gift; and I doubt not, that though thou hast long looked for its appearing, 'twill even now be somewhat of a surprise."

Then Master Dean openeth the cover, and lo! beneath it a book, of a folio size, somewhat thin. And he read aloud the title page, which, being in Latin, I shall here set down in English.

"THE NEW TESTAMENT OF OUR LORD AND SAVIOR JESUS CHRIST, Brought forth under the care of Desiderius Erasmus."

When he had read this we all sat silent for a space. Then said Master Colet: "What if some learned man should render this book, wherein are the very words of Christ and His Apostles, into our English tongue; and this dream also of thine, Master More, come true, and every child shall learn to read it!"

But Master More shook his head as one that doubted. "Thou rememberest that there are therein many things hard to understand, which the unlearned wrest to their own destruction."

"Yea, but it was of the unlearned that the gospel was first preached and first received," answered Master Colet.

As for me, I held my peace. But I do not doubt in my heart that Master Colet's words shall come true. For what end can there be to the multiplying of books by this new art of printing? And what book should be multiplied rather than this? And if books be multiplied what shall hinder the people from reading? And as for the rendering of the book into English it hath been done already, though not from the original tongue, by Baeda, surnamed the Venerable, and by others; and that it shall be done wholly and from the original itself, as indeed is fitting, I am assured. And though I live not to see this, for I am old, and there are yet many who are of Master More's way of thinking, yet now I rejoice to have looked upon this book. It is well that the printer take the place of the scribe, if he can give such a gift to Christian men. And here I end my writing in this book.

THE EPILOGUE, WRIT BY THOMAS BINGHAM

The 1st day of March, 1559.

I, THOMAS BINGHAM, who add to this book what hereinafter followeth, will say at this present only so much of myself, that I was of the kindred of Thomas Aylmer, sometime chantry priest of Barnet, being grandson to his sister, and that I was a monk of the monastery of St. Alban at the time of its dissolving, and was thereupon assigned a pension of nine marks by the year.

The said Thomas Aylmer died in the year 1530, being then ninety years of age, weak indeed of body, but of so sound a mind that neither memory nor apprehension had at all failed him. Nevertheless for five years before his decease he had a deputy in his chantry, not being able himself to sing mass; and he had himself dwelt in the house of a gentleman of Hadley, Francis Goodere by name, who gave to his old age kindly and honourable shelter.

I was present at his decease (which befell on the last day of September in the year aforesaid), having been fetched for that cause from the monastery. It was eleven in the forenoon when I came into his presence. He lay upon his bed very calm and peaceful, having already confessed and received absolution, and been fortified with the sacraments. There were gathered in his chamber Master Francis Goodere and Mistress Alice his wife, and Henry and Dorothy, their son and daughter. Then the old man called for his monk's scrip, and bade Master Goodere open it, for he himself was too feeble so much as to move a hand. "What money findest thou therein, son Francis?" for so he called Master Goodere. And he said, "Four marks or thereabouts." Then the old man said, smiling the while, "See now, my son, how thou with thy bounty hast caused me to break my vow of poverty. Lo! I am cumbered with riches, and must needs make a will and testament. But it shall be such as the Latins did call nuncupatoria, that is, made by word of mouth. Let the parson of Hadley have a mark, and if he will, let him say a mass or twain for my soul. And let the parson of South Mimms, in which parish my chantry is locally situate, have the same. The two marks that remain I give to Henry and Dorothy Goodere, one to each, desiring them, if it be their pleasure, to buy therewith some ring or trinket whereby they may remember me. The little book in writing I give to my nephew, Thomas Bingham, to whom also I bequeath the half of all other books or volumes, whether in writing or print, of which I am possessed, and the remainder Francis Goodere shall have. And lest ye two fall out over this great inheritance, I will that Master Goodere shall first choose one of the books which he shall like best, and then Thomas Bingham another, and so forth till all be divided. Let the other small matters in the bag, the comb and the knife and the like, be divided among the serving men and women. And I give to Henry Goodere my angling tackle (if any of it yet survives) and to Dorothy Goodere my brushes and colours and other implements of painting. And now, son Francis, take from the bag a little packet sealed that thou wilt find lowest of all." So Master Goodere brought it forth. Then said the old man, "Open it!" and to himself, "It were no harm to see it once more before I die." So Master Goodere brake the seal and opened it. And within, wrapped in three folds of paper, was a little kerchief of white linen; and we noted that it had a smell of lavender. Then the old man said, speaking as it were to himself, "She bound it on my finger, which I had wounded with a knife, cutting a rose in the garden; and I have not seen it for threescore years and nine." And then to Master Goodere, "Fold it again and lay it upon my breast when I am buried." Now none of us knew what this might mean, but now, having read the little book, I know. After this he lay for the space of half an hour or so, speaking in a low voice of persons and places that he had seen in time past, for so it seemed to us that stood by, though the names were for the most part unknown to us. Last of all, opening his eyes, for before he had lain as one that slept, and looking up, as though he saw somewhat, he said, "Sunt sicut angeli in coelis," and drawing his breath twice deeply, so departed.

He had, as they who have read this book do know, but few of the things that men commonly desire; but he had that wherein shall be found the best riches, a quiet and contented spirit; nor do I, who knew him from my childhood, remember so much as one word of complaint upon his lips. And he had also this happiness, that though he perceived the evil that was coming upon the houses of religion in this land, he saw it not with his own eyes. Six years thereafter the smaller houses were dissolved, and in three years more the same thing befell all that yet remained. I do not deny that there needed to be brought about some change. For indeed these houses were too many by far, and had too great riches, holding, it was commonly reported, one-third of the land of this nation. Also they were too much given to idleness, having altogether lost their old love of letters and sound learning; nor were they altogether pure—for how should men so be that lived in idleness?—from other sins (though these were falsely magnified). But it was an ill deed that bolstered up with their possessions the houses of nobles, ignorant men for the most part, and greedy of riches and pleasures. For if it was to the good of the commonwealth, as indeed I deny not, that these great possessions should be taken from their then present holders, yet should they have been still preserved to the service of God, being given to schools and the like, and for the better aiding of the poor. This was not done; but rather (if I may speak plainly) these great riches were given over, for the most part, to the service of the devil, going to feed the riotous living of a pack of godless courtiers.

Of the monastery of St. Alban there is little to be told. In the year 1540 John Boreman, who had been chosen abbot two years before, did, after some vain show of resistance, surrender the abbey to the King. And, indeed, how could he have done otherwise. For not only had he been put in his place for this end, being, as was believed, of a pliant disposition, but he could not have withstood to any purpose had he been so minded. But Master Boreman was not of the temper of Abbot Whiting of Glastonbury, that was hanged by King Henry the Eighth, but was content to have his pension of four hundred marks.

It was an evil day when we were driven forth from our home, though we had, as I have said, some provision made; but that which I was most disturbed to see was the fury with which the townsfolk fell upon the buildings, destroying them, not only for greed, but as it would seem, from very hatred. Nor could I but confess to myself that, though they were not blameless, we had not been so hated had we borne ourselves more like Christian men and better kept our vows.

There is no need to tell at length how I have fared between the dissolving of the abbey and this present time of writing. Let it suffice to say that being able to write a legible hand I could earn so much with the scriveners as with my pension sufficed to keep me without stinting. In the last year of King Henry the chantries were granted to the King and the priests turned out. As for that of which my uncle was priest, it lay empty for a long space, but was not pulled down, as were many in those days, the Barnet folk preserving it for a memorial of the great battle. And indeed in Queen Mary's time, there was talk of restoring it, but the land had been bestowed elsewhere, and nothing was done. Then, when her majesty Queen Elizabeth came to the throne, I, thinking that it might be turned to some good purpose, and having some interest with persons in authority, procured it to be granted to me on a lease, and have made it into a house for travellers. Nor have I done this, lest haply some should think it a profaning of things given to sacred uses, without good advice first taken from such as are able to judge of such matters. That it should be turned again to its old uses is manifestly a thing not to be expected; and I conceive that this being so, it is more to the honour of God that it should give shelter to the weary and destitute than that it should stand desolate, falling little by little into decay. As for myself, I do it not for gain, but conceive that I shall so best keep the vow wherewith I bound myself in my youth to God's service. I blame not others that have gone into the world, to which indeed they were constrained without other choice, and have gathered substance and taken to themselves wives. But I am rather content to abide in the state whereto I was once called; and having been driven forth from one house of God, to make to myself another by prayer and such good deeds as He may give me grace to do.

The End

Milton Keynes UK
Ingram Content Group UK Ltd.
UKHW010704260923
429409UK00004B/356